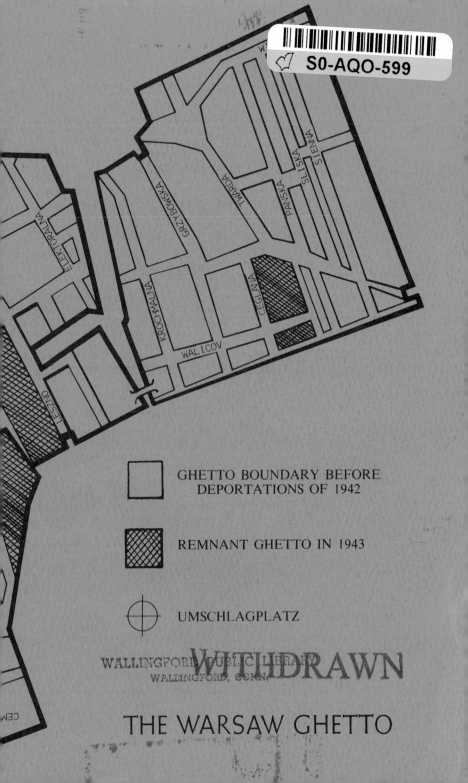

S0-AQO-599

☐ GHETTO BOUNDARY BEFORE
   DEPORTATIONS OF 1942

▨ REMNANT GHETTO IN 1943

⊕ UMSCHLAGPLATZ

WITHDRAWN

THE WARSAW GHETTO

Janusz Korczak, born Henryk Goldszmidt, was an elderly physician who had achieved world-renown as one of Poland's greatest writers and educators. By the age of thirty he had given up a successful medical practice and the possibility of a family of his own to start the Our Home orphanage for Jewish children in Warsaw, "to have many children, to replace their parents, and to prove there was love and justice in the world." When the Germans conquered Poland in 1939, Korczak and his orphans were moved to the Warsaw ghetto. Three years later the Treblinka II extermination camp was opened, and each day over 5,000 Jews were shipped in freight cars from Warsaw to its gas chambers. Week by week the ghetto grew smaller, the wall aroung it tightened, and the daily exportation of Jews increased, first to 7,000 and then to 10,000.

Despite rumors of extermination that filtered back into the ghetto, the people refused to believe what was happening. Even after the Jewish underground had proof that the resettlement trains were headed for Treblinka, the ghetto Jews were still incredulous. "This refusal to accept the terrible facts was what kept the weak from despair," wrote Korczak, "the crutch of illusion essential to the survival of human dignity." But the leaders of the underground believed

(*continued on back flap*)

A
Field
of
Buttercups

by

Joseph Hyams

Prentice-Hall, Inc., Englewood Cliffs, N.J

127607

£ 4.63

A FIELD OF BUTTERCUPS by Joseph Hyams
© 1968 by Joseph Hyams

Library of Congress Catalog Card Number: 68-27840
Printed in the United States of America   T
Prentice-Hall International, Inc., London
Prentice-Hall of Australia, Pty. Ltd., Sydney
Prentice-Hall of Canada, Ltd., Toronto
Prentice-Hall of India Private Ltd., New Delhi
Prentice-Hall of Japan, Inc., Tokyo

For Elke

CONTENTS

A Field of Buttercups

✡

✡   BOOK ONE   ✡

✡

1

THE SPRING OF 1942 DRESSED WARSAW'S PARKS IN GREEN AND softened the hard outlines of the monuments that had been erected by past conquerors—Swedes, Russians, Prussians, Germans. Once again German troops held Poland, but the cherry trees were in blossom along the banks of the Vistula and peasants plowed the fields outside the city. People savored the sun-warmed air and for a moment forgot the war, the shattered buildings, the green-clad troops in every street.

But the spring's promise of renewal could not pass a grim brick wall, nine feet high and two bricks thick, its top studded with broken glass, which lay on the left bank of the Vistula. The wall—eleven miles long—isolated 1,000 acres of the city of Warsaw and enclosed 400,000 Jews in an ancient slum of grimy tenements, built for the most part around central courtyards.

The wall had been erected with Jewish money. The Germans taxed the Jews to pay a German construction firm which used forced Jewish labor. There were twenty-two entrances from other sections of the city, guarded by German and Polish policemen. Only Jews who could prove absolute necessity for leaving received permits to do so. The death penalty was applied to those caught leaving the ghetto without permits.

For the Jews crammed into the ghetto even bare survival was illegal, since it was impossible to stay alive for long on the official ration of eight hundred calories a day, consisting largely of bread, potatoes, and ersatz fat.

Behind the wall the imprisoned Jews tried with every device of creative imagination to lead a civilized life. And nowhere in the ghetto was this attempt to continue the flow of normal activity more dedicated than in Our Home, an orphanage for two hundred children. Their ages ranged from five to fourteen years. Their parents, for the most part, had been killed by typhus, starvation, or German bullets. The children had in common only their Jewish heritage.

Musik had been born in Paris, the illegitimate child of a Polish prostitute of Jewish descent. The girl came back to Warsaw with her child for the funeral of her parents just before the German invasion. Stuck in Warsaw without money, she took up her old profession in the whore's section near Krochmalna Street in the old ghetto.

Unable to earn enough money to feed herself and Musik, she decided it was time that the boy, then eleven years old, become a breadwinner. Borrowing a baby carriage and baby from a neighbor, she dressed Musik in his most ragged clothes and sent him onto the street to beg. The baby was almost starved to death and continually crying, and to make Musik even more pitiable his mother tied his right arm inside his jacket so he would appear to be crippled.

She then walked a little behind them on the streets, plying her own trade and at the same time keeping track of the money given to Musik, who was to turn around periodically. If his mother was not in sight he was to stay where he was and wait. Sometimes it would be an hour—sometimes half a day—before his mother returned. Often she was drunk and gave him a beating for the money she claimed he had kept in her absence.

Because they lived on Krochmalna Street, Musik passed in front of the orphanage often enough to envy the children, obviously better fed than he, playing together in the courtyard in front of the building. The children soon noticed the ragged beggar-boy who always looked with such longing at their games. It was Irene who first called Dr. Korczak's attention to him. Over a period of months the doctor and Musik became nodding acquaintances: Musik knew who the doctor was but Korczak knew nothing about the ragged child.

One night Musik's mother disappeared. The baby's mother told him she had been picked up by the Germans for questioning, but he overheard a neighbor snickering that she had gone where the money was—to a German officer's brothel on the Aryan side. Musik waited three days for his mother to return. At the end of the third day without food he went to the orphanage on Krochmalna Street and told Albert, the porter, he had to see Dr. Korczak on a matter of urgency.

When Korczak arrived at the porter's office, he found Musik had fainted from hunger. It required a week of careful nursing before the doctor learned even part of the story. His inquiries in the boy's old neighborhood revealed the rest. Unlike most of the children at the orphanage who had at least one living relative nearby, Musik was without anyone.

Dr. Korczak accepted Musik into the orphanage and sent him through the standard routine: bath, head shaved, clean clothes. He assigned Musik a bed in the younger boy's dormitory and arranged for one of the older boys to be his guide and counselor; every younger child was the responsibility of an older one, and the elder had to make weekly reports on his ward's progress.

Adziu had scars even deeper than those that disfigured his face.

When the passports of emigrating Polish Jews were revoked by the German government in 1938 and the refugees were all returned to the Polish border, his family was caught up in the general expulsion. The story was well covered in the world press. On the first night the Jews were deported to Czechoslovakia. The next day the Czechs deported them to Hungary, then they were shipped to Germany and back to Czechoslovakia again, only to be rounded up by the Germans and examined for "selection."

Adziu's father was separated from the family in Czechoslovakia. He was a strong young man who hoped he could find safety for his family in France. An SS officer ended those plans. With a flick of his swagger stick Adziu's father was sent to a work battalion. The rest of the family was put on a cattle car for Auschwitz in Poland for "resettlement."

On the train, Adziu's mother, a soft-spoken but determined woman, managed to retain a grip on her eleven-year-old son and nine-year-old daughter. She fought her way to the side of the car near the overhead air vents. A Lithuanian guard was on top of the car. She waved her diamond engagement ring at him and pointed to her children. He nodded his agreement.

Hugging her children to her she knelt down and whispered to Adziu. "You are a man now, and you must take care of your sister. When you leave the train you must hide. And you must promise me that you will never get on a train again." Then, embracing and kissing her children for the last time, she took the diamond ring off her finger and gave it to Adziu. "Give this to the guard on top of the train when you get there."

She lifted the girl up on her shoulders so that the guard could grasp her hands. And then it was Adziu's turn. He barely had time to give the guard the ring before he was hurled like a sack of potatoes off the moving train.

Adziu fell sprawling, face first, to the ground below. Sharp stones cut deep into his face, but he had strength enough to crawl away from the tracks into the woods nearby. A group of Polish partisans riding past on a cart heard his moans and went to investigate. Before he fainted from pain and shock, Adziu told them to look for his sister. The partisans had no doctor, but one of the women treated Adziu's cuts with a brew of herbs. He recovered, but the terrible scars remained.

For a year Adziu and his sister lived with the partisans in the savage Bieszczady mountains in the southeastern corner of Poland. His sister, who had not been seriously hurt in the fall, helped with the cooking. Adziu became a scout. He used to steal into villages at night. The next day, looking like any ragamuffin village boy, he helped the German military detachments, carried water for their horses or polished boots, and then sneaked off to bring whatever information he had gathered back to the partisans.

There was still snow on the ground when the band of partisans discovered that the Germans had surrounded them on three sides, with a swamp at their rear. The partisans tried to fight their way out but were driven back and forced to retreat into the marshes.

The Germans followed. For two days and three nights Adziu hid with the partisans in the swamp, without food, ducking under the muddy water when patrols got too near. Some of the partisans were caught and shot, others drowned or died of exposure, but many, including Adziu, somehow survived.

Soon the boy became experienced enough at partisan tactics to be taken out on real jobs—blowing up bridges and trains. One day the partisans were informed that a German troop train was due to pass on a nearby track. They carefully buried three mines and laid concealed wires a hundred yards to a camouflaged dugout. Adziu was given the privilege of pushing the handle on the detonator. The explosion he triggered and the mopping up afterward gave him nightmares for weeks.

Once the partisans captured a German soldier. They told Adziu to avenge his mother and father by burning out the German's eyes. "They do it to us," the partisan chief, Gridzu, told Adziu.

Gridzu put the German's own bayonet in the campfire until the steel was glowing. Taking Adziu by the hand he led him to the tree where the soldier had been tied. The German saw them coming with the bayonet and screamed for mercy.

Two partisans grasped the man's head and held it steady. Gridzu pushed the point of the blade into an eye socket. The German, his face streaming blood, fainted.

Adziu vomited and tried to run away. Gridzu called him an unworthy son. He put the bayonet in Adziu's hands, and with his own large hand covering Adziu's he guided the point into the soldier's other eye.

"You have avenged your parents," Gridzu said. "I am proud of you."

Adziu was twelve.

Before the end of the year detachments of the Russian Army occupied the area and the partisans decided to disband. The wife of one asked Adziu's sister to stay with them as their daughter. Adziu elected to go off on his own to search for his mother. He wandered deeper into Poland until he reached Warsaw, where he lived as a street beggar for three months. One day Dr. Korczak saved him from a beating by a man he had annoyed by his persistence. Korczak brought Adziu back to the orphanage, deloused him, cut his hair, fed him, and assigned him a cot. For the first night in almost two years Adziu slept in a bed. Adziu had found a home, but he still searched every face on the streets looking for his mother. And he kept a bayonet hidden under his mattress.

Although Abrasha was only thirteen years old he was already somewhat of a legend at the orphanage: the story was that he had been born with a violin in his hands. Actually, he had started to play when he was four. He picked up his grandfather's violin one day, tucked it under his chin, and bowed the strings with a squeak. His proud grandfather was convinced that the boy had natural talent. He was right. Abrasha was one of the rare ones, a born musician.

When he was nine, his father presented the boy to a board of review at the Warsaw Conservatory of Music and asked for an appraisal of his son's talent. For the occasion Abrasha played the third movement of the Brahms Double Violin Concerto plus a composition of his own creation devised solely to display the facility of his short but supple fingers.

The review board was unanimous in forecasting a brilliant future for the boy, but it suggested he continue his private studies until he reached the age of fifteen.

Then, if his talent lived up to its promise, they pledged to accept him as a scholarship student.

"But there must be more to his childhood than music," an old professor warned the father. "The boy must live in the world too. He must experience all normal emotions if he is to bring heart and feeling to his music."

Abrasha's parents were killed by the SS during a "riot" on Grzybowska Street. Abrasha, carrying his violin case, was brought to the orphanage by his aunt. She told Korczak of his family's death and the fact that he was a prodigy. "But he has not touched the violin since they were killed," she said. "Nor has he spoken a word."

Abrasha made no protest when his head was shaved, said nothing when he was introduced to everyone at dinner on his first night as a new member of the family. But not once did he let go of the violin case. He took it to bed with him, carried it into the toilet, laid it carefully by his bed at night. But the other children accepted Abrasha's peculiarity without question. Most of them treasured souvenirs of happier times: a colored stone collected on a long-ago family picnic, an article of clothing worn by their parents. These were their only links with the past, and each of them remembered how hard it was to fit into life in the orphanage at the beginning.

One day while Abrasha was in the W.C., Musik snatched the violin case away and ran into the boy's dormitory waving it over his head, with Abrasha in fierce pursuit. Musik had only time enough to get the case open and take the violin out before Abrasha was on him crying, kicking, and punching.

Halinka, a small, pretty girl with high cheek bones and huge, almond-shaped eyes, broke up the struggle.

11

Halinka's father had been killed in Russia. Her mother had been raised by Korczak, and the doctor was her godfather. Halinka rescued the violin, before it was damaged, by threatening to bring Musik up before the Children's Court if he did not put it down at once.

The other children left the room, but Halinka stayed to comfort Abrasha, who lay on his cot, sobbing, clutching his violin. She cradled his head in her lap and after a while Abrasha stopped crying and looked up at her. He said nothing, but got up and tenderly took the violin from its case.

Tucking it underneath his chin he began to play Brahm's Lullaby. He smiled at Halinka, who sat mesmerized by the music. Then he played "Czarda" and made the violin sing his thanks to her.

When the other children, hearing the music, trooped back into the room, Abrasha stopped playing and placed the violin carefully back in its case. But now he had a bond with Halinka.

"That's all it takes," said Dr. Korczak when he heard of the incident. "All Abrasha needed was to have one person show love for him again."

The next day he took Abrasha to the potato cellar under the orphanage and told him he could practice there whenever he wished. For weeks Abrasha went alone to the cellar every day and practiced. But he still didn't speak. The violin spoke for him.

One afternoon Miss Esther prevailed on him to play the violin in the study hall upstairs while she accompanied him on the piano. At first they were alone during these sessions. Then children began to drift quietly into the room to listen. Soon Abrasha played for special occasions. He gave a brief recital before each play that was put on at the orphanage and everyone, even Musik, understood that he had a special talent. And always, in the front row of the audience, was Halinka.

One day early in July Abrasha stood in the hallway outside of the recreation room. He slowly pushed open the door to the room to see if Halinka was there.

She was at a table in a corner of the room working with Miss Esther. Some of the younger children were building houses out of blocks by the doorway, but there were no older boys around.

Timidly Abrasha entered the room holding his violin stiffly at his side. He stepped carefully over a castle of blocks and approached the table.

"Won't you play 'Home, Sweet Home' for us?" Miss Esther asked.

Abrasha nodded mutely and, taking the violin from its case, tucked it under his chin while Miss Esther sat down at the piano.

They played and the children sang. All of them were remembering living rooms and kitchens long since gone; mothers and fathers who were dead; toys and tender kisses in the night which existed now only in dreams from which they awoke crying.

Once, during the song, Abrasha glanced at Halinka. She had stopped sewing and was smiling sadly at him.

"I have another song that I would like to play," said Abrasha, the first words he had spoken in almost six months. "I would like to dedicate it to Halinka. Its name is: 'The Prayer of a Jewish Child.'"

13

Abrasha spoke deliberately, as though he had memorized his speech. Miss Esther, who realized how important this moment was for Abrasha, concealed her surprise and pleasure. As though conversation with Abrasha was an everyday affair, she asked him if he had a score for her to accompany him.

Abrasha shook his head. He took from his violin case a piece of paper on which he had neatly written his composition. He solemnly gave it to Halinka.

Then he played, and the music from his violin seemed to fill the orphanage. It was haunting, sad, and then it became a spirited Jewish hora. Suddenly, as he neared the climax, a string broke. For a measure Abrasha tried to continue playing without it, but it was no use. He stopped and, ashen-faced, looked at Halinka.

"I'm sorry," he said, on the verge of tears. "I just can't finish it without the E string, and I have no other."

"Perhaps we can find another E string for you," Miss Esther said.

Abrasha refused to be comforted.

"Can you sing the rest of the piece to me?" Halinka asked.

"No," said Abrasha, tucking the violin back into its case. "This is my voice." They were the last words he was to speak for eight weeks.

Not all of Korczak's orphans were under his roof. During the thirty years he had been running orphanages in Poland he had been a father-figure to more than three

14

thousand children. One of them, now an adult, was trying to sleep on the fifth floor of the Metropole Hotel in the Aryan section of Warsaw.

SS Obersturmfuehrer Erwin Schneider had spent a tiring three days on the train going from the Eastern Front to Warsaw. Outside of his room, in the corridor, he heard muted Polish voices. For years, he had successfully blocked from his consciousness the memory of a time in his life now triggered by the hushed sounds in the corridor, and he felt the terrible loneliness of awakening from a nightmare.

He had been sitting between his mother and father on the front seat of their new black Opel which his father had bought especially for their summer vacation. They had reached Warsaw only that morning and were driving to their hotel when the accident happened. It all came into focus again: the truck bearing down on them, his mother throwing her body across his. The crash. The silence.

He awoke in a bed covered with white, a white screen cutting off the world outside. He was on his back staring at the paint peeling off the ceiling, and in the air was a sharp smell he later learned was ammonia. The screen was pulled aside and a doctor and nurse came to the side of his bed. It was weeks before the words they said became reality: his parents were dead.

Now they wanted to know the name of a relative who could come and get him. He kept his face rigid and shut his eyes to block out the vision he had of his mother's brother, a powerful man with a saber-scarred face who always wanted to take him to a gymnasium to develop his body. "We need strong bodies for the future," he would say as he pinched Erwin's thin arms. He remembered his aunt; tall as her husband, thin and sour. "She's from the Schwartzwald in the southwest," his father once explained. "That's how they are there—cold. You mother's a rare exception." The aunt never smiled, never laughed, never had children, though she was full of ideas about raising them properly to be cultured young Germans.

"I can't remember any relatives," he told them.

Later he heard the doctor tell the nurse that he probably had amnesia. "He's well enough to be discharged," the doctor said. "The best we can do is send him to the municipal orphanage until we can find a relative."

At the mention of orphanage he wanted to scream out his uncle's name, but he clenched his teeth and remained silent.

He was silent for most of the time he was at the orphanage on Cedrowa Street. He never cried when the other children tormented him with names like Kraut, Donnerwetter, and Hun. He was silent too on the day that Dr. Korczak discovered some of the older boys had stuffed him into a wooden packing case, then nailed down the lid, using stones as hammers.

Later that night, though, the tears that had been welling up inside him since the death of his parents gushed out and he sobbed for hours. He went to sleep while the doctor rocked him gently in his arms and told him a fairy tale in German.

2

THE MAN RESPONSIBLE FOR THE ORPHANS, JANUSZ KORCZAK, was a frail, elderly physician who had achieved world renown as an educator and writer. Giving up the possibility of a family of his own, Korczak had long ago decided instead to have many children, to replace their parents, and to prove there was love and justice in the world. Before the Nazi occupation of Poland he had founded two orphanages which bore his name; one in Bielany, a suburb of Warsaw, and another in the heart of the city. After the occupation the orphanage at Bielany

17

was devoted exclusively to housing Christian children and Korczak decided to devote all of his attention to the welfare of his Jewish orphans. In the space of two years he had been forced to move the Jewish orphans each time the Nazis restricted the ghetto boundaries. They moved from Krochmalna Street to Chlodna Street and, finally, in June 1942 they were living in two floors in a corner house at the junction of Sienna Street and Sliska. The building had once been the clubhouse for the Guild of Merchants and there was a large banquet hall on the first floor which served as dormitory and focal point for orphanage life. At night the large room was divided by cupboards, with boys on one side and girls on the other. During the day the cupboards were pushed back against the wall and the cots folded up to make room for dining. Smaller adjacent rooms served as reading rooms, sewing rooms, and for Korczak a combination office, isolation ward, bedroom.

But the Home was fearfully crowded. Besides the two hundred children moved from the orphanage on Chlodna Street, the Home provided sleeping space for as many as fifty older ones who had lived at the orphanage in the past and now turned up in the evenings seeking shelter overnight.

As one of the few doctors in the ghetto, Korczak had become expert at calculating with dispassionate accuracy when people would die. As for himself, he knew he had less than a year to live. He was slowly starving: the organism was digesting its own protein and the muscles were disappearing.

Getting up in the morning meant standing upright, putting on his shirt and buttoning it up, at least two buttons. Then wrestling with his pants. His legs were so swollen and the skin on them so tightly stretched that he could scarcely bend his knees. The trousers and tunic he put on were all that remained of the Polish Army uniform he wore in the First World War. Though faded and shabby one could tell they had at least had a military history, but the shoes were an ugly product of ghetto ingenuity. They had uppers of fabric and soles of wood which made a curious tsak–tsak noise when he walked. Korczak was certain everyone noticed only his feet when they saw him. He had always been very particular about shoes; every time a new boy was admitted to the orphanage he insisted on teaching him the "proper technique" of shoe-shining. "The tips of the fingers must be used for rubbing in the wax, and it is permissible if not necessary to lightly spray the waxed shoe with saliva, which is then firmly brushed," he would say, demonstrating his technique. "Then, and only then, the cloth. Briskly. Purposefully."

Boots are the only suitable footwear for a uniform, he was thinking. He examined his face critically in a sliver of mirror. For years he had been nearsighted, but now middle-aged farsightedness had corrected the imperfection. The left lens of his steel-rimmed glasses was cracked so he had to tilt his head to look through a clear part of the glass. What he saw in the mirror was not reassuring. The skin not hidden by a ginger beard was the texture and color of a Kiev dumpling. His blue-gray eyes, the whites veined with red, were sunken in deep, black hollows from lack of sleep and constant hunger.

He could never understand why hair blossomed on the lower half of his face while there was not even a bud on top. Though not a vain man he sometimes wished that if he could not have been born taller than his five feet, nine inches, perhaps he could have been given hair that was more lasting or teeth that were less painful. Most of his teeth had been pulled during the 1914–18 campaign by a Russian dentist, a major, who gave him no anesthetic but told him to "be of good cheer." There were no dentists in the ghetto so he had taken to doing his own dental work as well as the children's. He had filed one of his own teeth to the nerve, and even now he shuddered at the memory.

Ordinarily his mornings began at six. He usually awakened in time to carry down the chamber pots—there were ten—and empty them before the children awakened. But on this day he was up at five.

Putting the mirror down carefully on his desk top, he tilted his head so he could get a clear view of the seven others who shared his small office-bedroom. They were still asleep on their newspaper-covered straw mattresses: the Germans had long ago confiscated all decent bedding. All the children here were ill. Both seven-year-old Genia and nine-year-old Felunia had pneumonia. The others, who had fever and diarrhea, were Monius the Younger (he had four Moniuses in the orphanage including the Elder, Junior, and Just Plain Monius), Albert, Georgie, and Hanezka. Sixty-year-old Azrylewicz, the tailor and father of Henryk, one of the children, was dying of angina pectoris. The old tailor, who now moaned softly in his sleep, would sit all day on the cot, feet hanging down heavily, his emaciated upper body anchored by a bony elbow.

Through his door he could see the boy's dormitory. A

little to the east slept sixty girls. Two hundred orphans, each with a mouth to be fed.

Alone in the empty dining room—the others would not awaken for another half hour—he drank a cup of ersatz coffee mixed with grounds, and meditated on his day; six calls to make, his usual rounds, how much food could he expect?

Before leaving he put on his legionnaire's Maciejowska cap, tugged to what he hoped was a jaunty angle. Then he reached into the pocket of his tunic and took out the black armband with a six-pointed yellow star in the center. He pulled the brassard carefully over his right sleeve, just above the elbow. He walked through the courtyard scarcely mindful of the old woman bent over a steaming washtub, an old Jew with a thin beard and a parchment-yellow forehead muttering over an open volume, a young man in a sweat-stained vest who held a stick of sealing wax to a candle and dabbed the heated end on an envelope.

The area was littered with filth; no cleanup services were allowed to operate in the ghetto. On Sliska there were two naked corpses lying along the edge of the cobblestoned street, only their faces covered with newspapers. The corpses had been carried to the street during the night to await the morning burial wagon. The bereaved relatives did not have the money or spiritual strength to go through with a funeral even if it could be arranged, a doubtful business at best since special permission had to be obtained. He had seen many such bodies on the street. Everyone had, just as everyone in the ghetto was familiar with the mounting mortality figures—Feb-

21

ruary: 1,023; March: 1,668; April: 2,555; May: 3,821. The statistics were terrible but the reality was even more terrible; each death was a reminder that every soul in the ghetto could look forward only to the same fate.

By the time he reached the corner of Chlodna and Zamenhofa Streets, Korczak was tired and hungry to the point of collapse. His legs felt like wooden sticks and for a moment he lost his balance and had to lean against a storefront. He saw a half-grown boy on the pavement, a fresh corpse. Nearby three boys were playing at being horses. The string they were using for harnesses caught on the body. It was difficult to disentangle and they were impatient to get on with the game. Finally, one of the boys said, "Let's move on. He's a nuisance."

Despite the bodies, noisy crowds filled the street, all wearing the six-pointed star on their arms or backs, elbowing their way through the throngs not touching each other with their hands for fear they might be touching typhus.

A woman who might have been anywhere from twenty to fifty years old, dressed in rags, with the glazed look of starvation in her eyes, pushed a baby carriage into his path. Pointing at two almost naked infants she intoned piteously, "Bread, a piece of bread." Ignoring her, Korczak checked for the third time the application for attendance at the orphanage of a boy at Smoczna 57. There were children in the courtyard, not playing, just there. They were no longer children, just prematurely aged beings with sorrowful, dull looks and legs like reeds. He climbed the staircase of the house—the railing had long ago been consumed for firewood—passing groups of

22

people on each landing lying on the floors without blankets or pillows. These were the homeless, who slept wherever there was a shelter.

The boy was the only descendant of two respectable families; only his mother and an aunt were still alive. Both families had shared a room in front of the building with a screen for the divider. The aunt told Korczak that she didn't think the boy would go to an orphanage. "Not until his mother is dead," she said. "She has stomach ulcers and there is no hope. But he's not here at the moment, he's on an errand."

On the other side of the screen the mother was lying on a sofa. "I can't die until I know he is looked after," she told Korczak. "He is such a good boy. He tells me I shouldn't sleep during the day because I won't be able to sleep at night. And at night he asks me why I groan. I tell him to pay no attention, but to go to sleep."

It was finally decided that on the weekend the aunt would bring the child to the orphanage. In the little book he carried in his pocket, Korczak made a notation to that effect with a pencil sharpened on both ends. As he was leaving the apartment, the mother thanked him. "Now I can die in peace," she said.

On the street in front of the apartment building Korczak saw an ordinary button lying just in front of him. He tried to bend over to pick it up but the effort made him dizzy. He finally crouched to the pavement and awkwardly retrieved it. The worthless button had value to Korczak. The children at the orphanage had no toys, and sometimes a button to play with could quiet a little one. He dropped it into his coat pocket.

23

A bicycle-powered rickshaw, the only vehicle in the ghetto other than official German cars, pedaled alongside Korczak. Such rickshaws had replaced horses as transportation, because it cost eighty zlotys a day to feed a horse and a man could live on twenty. So the horses were eaten and replaced by men. Korczak waved the man away. He had ridden in rickshaws during the first war while on service in Harbin, Manchuria, but no matter how tired he felt he could not bear to drain more strength from these half-starved souls on their clumsy handmade vehicles.

Suddenly there was running, shouting, and whistling—a warning that Germans were on the way. The street began to empty and every doorway was jammed with people trying to fight their way to shelter. A truck loaded with German police raced down the narrow street at full speed. It was almost noon and the guard at the Paviak Prison was being relieved. As the truck rolled by, the police leaned out to hit anyone within reach with rifle butts or clubs, shouting, "Dirty Jews, scabby typhus spreaders. . . ."

Korczak walked along Zelazna until he reached Chlodna Street, which divided the small ghetto from the large ghetto. A wooden bridge crossed over the street, and under the bridge, on the Aryan soil, was the Christian thoroughfare. Korczak hurried across because at the ghetto gate the German guards often directed little scenes of sadism. A favorite game was to seize some passing Jew at random and stand them in a line. Then the guards put bricks or heavy paving stones in their hands and ordered them to lift them up and down, up and down, urging

24

them on with blows, kicks, and obscenities. Roaring with laughter, they kept this up until the victims collapsed with exhaustion.

Almost every shabby house and courtyard he passed held memories for Korczak. Here along Panska Street, as a young doctor, he often made house calls for half a ruble, generally at night. For daytime visits in the more select suburbs of the city he charged from three to five rubles, as much as the established professors of medicine.

Halfway up Panska Street he encountered Selig Hartmish, head of a firm of bedmakers, talking with an associate on the street in front of his factory. Korczak burst in on the conversation.

"Ah, Mr. Hartmish," he said. "It occurs to me that you have not yet given a donation to the orphanage."

Hartmish looked at him scornfully. "That's right, Korczak," he said. "And I'm not likely to, either."

"Not likely to help the poor children of your community?" Korczak asked, trying to shame the man.

"That's right."

"But why? Don't you feel a responsibility for them?"

"I feel as much responsibility for them as you did for me," Hartmish said. "Do you remember when you fitted out your orphanage with beds?"

"Yes," said Korczak.

"Then you should also remember that you bought your beds from Konrad and Jarunszkiwicz. Why didn't you buy them from me?"

"For a very good reason," Korczak countered. "When we furnished the first Ophan's Home in 1911, we bought beds from Konrad and Jarunszkiwicz. That is true. But when we expanded the institution in 1920, we bought some beds from you."

Hartmish kept an uneasy silence.

"Now," said Korczak. "If you will be good enough to take a walk with me to Sliska Street, you will find all the beds from Konrad and Jarunszkiwicz still in perfect condition, while yours have long ago collapsed."

Hartmish glowered, seized his associate by the arm, and disappeared into his offices.

"I am the one who should be angry, not you, Hartmish," Korczak called after him. Then, as he started down the street, he thought to himself, "I have made another enemy. Why couldn't I have been tactful instead of honest?"

Along the wall of the Catholic church on Leszno Street he saw children with stomachs swollen from hunger and sores all over their bodies. Almost unconsciously he inventoried their symptoms: staring eyes, ulcerous lesions on the legs, scabies on their shaved heads. Their elders stood around them yellow and gaunt, pleading weakly, "A piece of bread . . . a piece of bread . . ."

There was a sudden commotion in the crowd. Someone shouted, "Catch him!" A barefoot, ragged boy darted out, tripped over a stone, and sprawled to the ground. In his hand he clutched a small bun. The owner of the bread, a street vendor, pounced on the boy and tried to tear the bread from his hands. But it had already been chewed and was wet with the child's saliva. The vendor gave the boy several hearty kicks and walked angrily away.

Korczak painfully knelt down by the child to see if he was hurt. The boy mistook the gesture. He had stolen the

26

bread and paid for it with a beating. He tried to bite Korczak's hand.

The young food-snatchers were a special category of ghetto criminal. Their hunger gave them desperation, and their youth gave them the agility to steal and run. They were savagely beaten both by the people they robbed and by the police. Often, Korczak knew, parents once law-abiding sent their children out to steal food and keep the family alive.

Some children were called "catchers." Boys would snatch packages from pedestrians and while still running would devour the contents. In their haste they sometimes stuffed themselves with soap or uncooked peas.

Many of the ghetto children were homeless orphans, and their number was growing every day. Singly and in packs they wandered through the courtyards and the streets, crying out their misery, looking like ragged ghosts. Standing alongside lampposts, by the walls of buildings, blocking the pavement, they kept repeating in a toneless voice that they were hungry. The musical among them sang in thin and feeble voices—often a popular ballad about a young soldier, mortally wounded and abandoned by everyone on the battlefield, who cried out in his agony, "Oh, mother!"

They tried everything possible to stir the conscience of the passersby. "Give us a slice of bread," they begged. "If you have no bread give us at least a potato or an onion so we may survive until tomorrow."

With dirty fingers they clung to the coats of passersby, and sometimes the more skillful and desperate children would use this as a cover to pick a pocket.

But on the same streets where he saw such scenes of horror, amid the swarms of tubercular children dying like flies, and alongside the corpses waiting for the scavanger wagons, Korczak passed stores full of fine foods, restaurants, and cafés which served the most expensive delicacies and drinks, smuggled from the other side. The clientele of these places consisted principally of Gestapo agents, Jewish police officials, rich merchants who did business with the Germans, smugglers, dealers in foreign exchange—the only ones who had money.

Feasting, drinking, and carousing was accompanied by a jazz band playing the popular hits all night. At dawn when the revelers left, the streets were strewn with paper-covered corpses blocking the paths. Human skeletons hovered like shadows begging in whispers for scraps of food. They were usually pushed aside for disturbing the complacency of the well-fed.

One of the worst nests of drunkenness and vice was the Esplanade Restaurant, favorite haunt of Jewish smugglers, which was near the end of the street Korczak was walking on. The street was blocked off by the wall. He had reached the limit of the ghetto. Beyond the wall was the Aryan Warsaw, where life was not easy either, but infinitely better than in the ghetto. There were no guards on the Jewish side of the wall, but the Aryan side was closely patrolled by police and SS men, all with the right to shoot without warning at anyone rash enough to come over it.

The last building before the wall was the Esplanade, approached by a flight of stairs from the street. On the top step was seated a rheumy-eyed old man dressed in filthy rags.

28

A rickshaw halted in front of the restaurant and an elegantly dressed woman alighted and made for the stairs. The beggar was sitting in such a position that it was impossible for her to pass without touching him or his rags. The woman, making no attempt to hide her disgust, impatiently gestured the begger to move over. "I can't walk over you," she said.

The beggar held out his hand. "How much?" he asked.

The woman, familiar with the procedure, threw him a groschen.

"Not enough," he said.

She dropped another coin. The beggar drew his legs in to let her pass, then immediately spread them across the doorway to block Korczak's entry.

Korczak felt his body tremble with anger at this sordid blackmail. Then he realized that he had much in common with the beggar. The hatred that raged against rich Jews as well as the poor was directed at them both. They were, in the eyes of the German conquerors, alike. And they were alike in another respect.

"I am a beggar just like you," said Korczak. "I have no money."

The beggar sneered. "You will get nothing in there, I promise you," he said, but he allowed Korczak to pass without payment.

This was the first time Korczak had been desperate enough to invade the Esplanade, and once inside he found it hard to believe his eyes. The walls had been painted red and were covered with mirrors. From the ceiling hung an elaborate crystal chandelier worthy of a palace. Waiters with white napkins draped over their arms hurried back and forth. Someone was playing a pianoforte. A girl with blond hair, her cheeks roughed, stood behind a buffet loaded with a variety of bottles, glasses, trays, and plates. Fresh, hot rolls were neatly stacked on the buffet, and every table had rolls on it. There was the smell of brandy, beer, roast meats, spices, and warm bread. Korczak could feel his head spinning as the glorious odor of food made him drunk with weakness and desire.

The girl at the buffet grinned, showing a mouthful of crooked teeth. Dazzled and shaken, he wanted to open the door and run out, but he had only strength enough to sit. Beside the buffet were three tables. He saw only one vacant seat, next to an elderly couple eating greedily. The man, who had a napkin tucked in his collar, was bent over a plate of meat, making a clatter with his knife and fork. His wife was shredding a roll into her soup.

"May I?" asked Korczak, pointing to the vacant chair.

Thinking that he wanted to remove the chair, the man nodded and continued eating.

Korczak sat down at their table and, paying no attention to their surprise, said rapidly, "Forgive me for interrupting your pleasure, but my errand is urgent and grave. Two hundred orphans whom I care for are going hungry, and I beg you to help them. I hope that those who are full of food will understand those who are hungry."

The man looked up in annoyance.

"Excuse me," said Korczak. "Perhaps you have not yet had your fill? In that case I will wait until you have finished."

He stared at them as they ate, and his hand almost

unconsciously moved toward the plate with warm rolls. The woman noticed the movement and said, not unkindly. "Would you like a roll?"

Her husband gave his wife an angry look but Korczak had quickly taken a roll and bit it; now it could not be taken back. He chewed the small piece slowly and pocketed the remainder. "For my children," he explained.

The man glared angrily at him. "What orphans are you collecting for? For your own pocket, I expect. Let me see your papers."

Korczak produced his identity card. "My name is Janusz Korczak," he said. "I don't know whether that means anything to you, but I am director of the orphanage at Sliska 19."

His name obviously did mean something to the couple because the man was reduced to red-faced silence. He reached for his pocketbook and produced five zlotys. "And I'll give you five zlotys a month from now on," he said. "In case I forget call me." He gave Korczak his card.

Korczak thanked them, and apologized for interrupting their meal. Such chutzpah, he said, was unforgivable in these elegant surroundings, but it was the result of nerves, the nerves of a man who had two hundred children to feed.

Strengthened by the bit of roll and encouraged by the five zlotys, Korczak entered a second room—a gaming room where a number of men were playing cards. He walked to the table and stood behind one of the players. He was accepted as just another kibitzer until, in a loud voice, he repeated his request for help for his two hundred orphans.

One of the gamblers impatiently waved him away with his hand. "Is there no place where we are free from beggars?" he asked the room at large.

"I'm not a beggar, I'm an asker," said Korczak.

"It's the same thing, and this isn't the place for it," said the gambler.

Korczak's humility and calm suddenly abandoned him. "In that case I shan't ask, I demand," he shouted. "I demand a contribution to the funds of the Jewish orphanage. That's your duty."

The players coldly ignored him and his outburst and continued their game. Korczak thumped his fist on the table, causing the chips to jump. Two of the men wearily got to their feet, prepared to do away with this annoying reminder of the world outside. Korczak faced them defiantly. He had been thrown out of such places often.

"Wait," one of the men at the table said suddenly. "I know this man. It's Janusz Korczak. Right?"

Korczak nodded.

"Who's he," another asked.

"You know, the writer," said his companion.

"What's a writer doing begging for Jewish orphans?"

"I am not begging, I am asking for food for the orphans who are my responsibility," said Korczak again.

"All right, let's make a collection for his kids," said the gambler who recognized Korczak. "Then we can get back to the game in peace." He put two zlotys in the center of the table. The others grudgingly followed suit; all but one.

"Why should I give money to someone I don't know?"

he asked. "I work hard for my money, and who knows when I will need every penny of it."

"Aren't you ashamed, Solomon," teased one of his companions. "You're the richest of us all. Fancy loving money so much."

Solomon shrugged. "Why not love money?" he asked. "This fellow loves children. Well, I love my children. Every hundred-zloty note is like a child to me."

Korczak laughed. "I appreciate your paternal feeling," he said. "I don't want to deprive you of your children. But I thank the rest of you sincerely in the name of my two hundred children."

He took the money from the table and walked out of the room toward the street. He was just opening the door when Solomon caught up with him. "Here," he said. "Here's two of my children." He put two more bank notes in Korczak's hand.

3

THE TWO-SEATER FIESELER STORCH OBSERVATION PLANE WITH the black cross on its fuselage flew over the flat lowlands at little more than stalling speed. Its shadow danced along some twelve hundred feet below as the plane slowly glided across the Vistula River, where the only traffic was a coal barge on its way from Silesia.

Twenty seconds later the plane was over the large patches of green that were Warsaw's famous parks. Nearby was the dark rectangle identified as the District of Jewish Residence on the 1:100,000-scale survey map the plane's passenger held on his lap.

34

SS Sturmbannfuehrer Dr. Ludwig Hahn sat rigidly straight. His eyes, peering through flying goggles, registered every detail as he studied the landscape below.

As the plane circled lazily, the general would look down, then carefully outline a small area on the map he held. Here a building, there a whole block—areas to be evacuated of Jews. When the area was cleared, he decided, he would put a cross in the center. Within the month he planned to mark a giant X over the entire area. The Warsaw ghetto would exist no longer.

Although his markings seemed to be without pattern, they were deliberately selected, spaced far enough apart so that no one section of the ghetto would be depleted at once. The ghetto would not be fully aware of what was happening until it was too late to resist. As Gestapo Chief of Warsaw, Hahn was responsible for the orderly evacuation of the ghetto and the eventual extermination of its population. The first step was to take place on this same morning, Tuesday, July 21, 1942, which was, not coincidentally, also Tishah b'Ab, the Jewish holiday commemorating the destruction of the temple at Jerusalem. Like a good hunter Hahn liked to catch his prey off guard, and today the Jews would be commemorating the ancient tragedy.

The plane's shadow disappeared in the dark ghetto roofs. From his vantage point the general could see the entire ghetto: half a million Jews compressed into a seething mass by the red brick wall.

Proceeding directly along the wall in a westerly direction the plane flew over the railroad station, the Umschlagplatz. Hahn tapped the pilot on the shoulder with his gloved left hand and made a circling motion with his finger. The plane circled slowly. Below was a train of forty cars on a siding—enough to handle the first shipment of Jews who would be arriving at the station the next morning. Hahn allowed himself a tight smile at this evidence of sound planning. He tapped on the pilot's shoulder to signal continuation of the tour. The plane swung back to the south following the railroad tracks. They were over a barren area studded with gray stones— the Jewish cemetery.

The general had a personal belief that a community's morale, and therefore its resistance, could be determined by an examination of its cemeteries and burial practices. Twenty months ago the Jews had buried their dead with services and ceremony. When the number of dead increased, the ceremonies became shorter. Now, he noted with satisfaction, the dead were buried in common graves. The traditional Jewish reverence had disappeared. The backbone of their culture was broken.

The pilot had almost reached the southeast edge of the ghetto when Hahn tapped his shoulder and pointed down. The plane dropped lower over a residential area of grimy three- and four-storied houses. There were occasional trees along the cobblestoned streets, which would soon be overflowing with a black stream of Jews, going to services.

They flew close to the corner building at Sliska and Sienna Streets. Sami and Halinka were carrying buckets out to the street, and other children were playing in the courtyard. They were excited at the sight of the plane so near, and several of them waved.

36

Hahn leaned out over the cockpit and waved a gloved hand in return. Then he reached into the upper right-hand pocket of his tunic. He took out a heavy black pencil and made a neat square on the map where the orphanage was located.

That night Korczak had a visitor in bed. Nine-year-old Sami had awakened with bad dreams. Korczak stroked the boy's forehead until he fell asleep again, but the cot was too small for them both. Carefully, Korczak scooped the boy up into his arms and carried him back into the dormitory. As he put him in his bed Sami awakened again. "What's the matter?" Korczak asked.

"I am afraid," Sami said, looking anxiously around the dark room.

"Afraid of what?" asked Korczak.

"I heard the Germans were coming to get us; to kill us," said Sami. "Just like what happened to the meshummadim."

"There's nothing to be afraid of," said Korczak. "I'm not going to let anything happen to you."

"But you're old," sobbed Sami. "What happens if you die, too?"

"I'm not as old as you think I am," Korczak said firmly. "Now I'm going back to my room to write. If you're frightened again, you can come back to me."

Korczak returned to his room. It was 3:00 A.M. and it had been a hard but profitable day. He and the children would continue to survive.

He set up the paper screen around his desk to avoid disturbing the sleepers, then laboriously lit the carbide lamp, the best light available in a ghetto deprived of gas, electricity, and kerosene. He located the pad on which he had written the subjects he was to talk about the following day with the older children in the eight to nine o'clock class. The children regularly prepared in advance a list of topics they wanted him to discuss, and he chose two or three.

1. The emancipation of women. 2. Hereditary traits. 3. Loneliness. 4. Napoleon. 5. What is duty? 6. The tasks of a doctor. 7. Amiel's diary. 8. London. 9. Mendel. 10. Leonardo da Vinci. 11. Faber. 12. Mind and understanding. 13. Genius and environment. 14. The Encyclopedists. 15. How did various authors write? 16. Nationality and cosmopolitanism. 17. Evil and malevolence. 18. Freedom, predetermination, and decision. 19. Some reminiscences of Dr. Korczak.

Outside he heard the sound of shots. From experience with the familiar echoes he knew they had been fired inside the ghetto walls, probably by the North Gate where the smugglers were most active. Cautiously he removed a thumbtack from the black paper covering the bedroom window, lifted a corner flap, and peeled it back several inches.

The window, like most in Warsaw, was a skillful mosaic. Almost all of the city's windows had been shattered during the German attack on the city. Skillful Jewish glaziers had pieced together small bits of glass with putty to make larger panes. The windows were hard to see through, but Korczak pressed his right eye to a clear spot and peered anxiously out. He could see nothing; the street was dark and quiet. But the shots had started his heart pounding and he was afraid, not of bullets but of the pain in his chest.

Regina's coughing brought him back to the present and as he carefully fastened the black paper into place his mind was busy with professional thoughts. Perhaps he had administered salicylates in an incorrect dosage. A spoonful every two hours brought on buzzing in the ears and temporary disturbance of vision. She ought by all rights to have vomited. All the same, the ulcers on her legs had grown smaller. In the case of children he was always anxious when it had anything to do with rhemuatism.

The pain in his tooth cut across his consciousness. There was no part of his body that did not ache. He had a painful carbuncle on his shoulder which needed to be lanced, a minor operation but one he could not perform on himself. He tried in vain to get one of the few doctors left in the ghetto to perform the operation, but they were all too busy with the seriously ill to be concerned with the the painfully ill.

In addition to the pain in his body, he was deteriorating mentally, his almost complete physical exhaustion making him distrustful and upset by trivialities. It required constant surveillance of every reaction to guard against snapping at the children, Mrs. Stefa (as the children called his unmarried assistant), or anyone else.

From time to time he escaped his physical and mental pain by taking cocaine. He described the narcotic's effect as "poorish. . . . Taken only to relieve pain and numb the senses—sending me into a semi-coma of dreams."

When his supply of cocaine ran out he resorted to

39

vodka. "Five thimblefuls of pure spirit with equal parts of hot water. Then the delightful sensation of drowsiness. . . ."

There was still a little vodka left and that might bring peace, but to reach it he would have to move the lamp, and that could awaken one of the children. In an attempt to forget the pain and the craving for vodka he focused his thoughts on a favored theme: what would he do if he survived? Perhaps, when the Nazis were finally defeated, the victors would call him up for service to build a new Europe or new Poland. That was unlikely—he was too old—and he didn't want it anyway because it meant he would have to be in an office job of some sort. The slavery of fixed working hours and a telephone. An enormous loss of time, wasted on banal issues, contesting little people with little ambitions, little nepotisms, and a great hierarchy with opposing goals. Altogether a donkey trot.

No, there were other younger, more flexible people for those jobs. All he wanted was that the children be left to him. A false ambition, he thought: to be a doctor and modeler of the childish soul. Soul. No more and no less. After the war, for convalescence and a little peace he would choose to go to the Children's Hospital where he could distribute sweets, tell fairy tales, and answer the most varied questions. That was the job for him, for the Old Doctor.

His mind gave itself over to his favorite daydream—one that had been recurrent since his first bout with enteric fever twenty years ago. He saw a great concert hall in America. People were coming in, dressed in handsome dark suits and colorful gowns. When the hall was filled he spoke eloquently of war, hunger, wretchedness, and orphaned children. Suddenly he was being showered with jewels, gold, money. Women threw their rings and necklaces onto the stage. His boys from the orphanage came on the platform and gathered them all up. They filled mattress covers with them. The audience clapped and shouted, weeping with emotion.

But the familiar fantasy did not have the usual effect of relaxing him. Instead, he was more awake than ever, and his mind began to dwell on an abominable dream he had had the night before. The Germans caught him without a Star in Praga. As they were carrying him away, cursing and kicking him, he had awakened to the sound of his heart pounding, his mind full of panic. He was afraid he was going to die there in bed, but he didn't want to die, wasn't ready. There was still too much to do.

On this night, when he finally did fall asleep, he had two dreams. In the first he was being dragged into a compartment full of Jews, mostly dead infants. One child without any skin was still breathing.

In the second dream he was on top of a ladder. His father was at the bottom pushing a piece of cake into his mouth. What he could not get into his mouth he put in the pocket of his jacket.

He woke up sweating, wondering if this was the way his death would come. He struggled to his feet and fumbled in the dark for the vodka and the water glass.

4

SAMI BROUGHT KORCZAK A LETTER TO READ AFTER THE younger children's Saturday morning discussion group. Thin and pale with dark, luminous eyes and black stubble on his shaved head, Sami was an organizer. Despite his unimpressive appearance the older boys already paid attention to him.

"Mister Doctor," Sami said, "could you please read this and see if it is well formulated?"

He held out a letter, carefully printed and enclosed in an envelope made by folding and pasting another piece of paper. The boy's eyes sparkled as Korczak read the letter which was addressed to the Right Reverend Vicar of the Church of All Hallows.

"We hereby respectfully request that we may be allowed to visit the churchyard on Saturdays early in the morning," the letter read. "We long for a little fresh air and the sight of green things. Our place is cramped and airless. We would like to have some contact with nature. We promise not to damage anything. We beg you earnestly to grant our request."

The letter was signed: Zygmunt, Sami, Abrasza, Hanka, and Aronek.

Korczak nodded seriously when he finished reading and declared it was a fine letter. When Sami asked if he and the other children could deliver it, Korczak agreed and said Miss Esther, his assistant, would go with them.

The children dressed in their Passover best: skirt and kerchief for Hanka, khaki shorts with white shirts and caps for the boys. Following a discussion about whether to wear their good shoes or their everyday sandals, it was finally decided they would wear the sandals in case they were allowed to play in the churchyard.

Esther escorted the children as far as the church and warned them that they were to hide, then run home if they saw any sign of police—German or Jewish. She watched anxiously as they entered the gate until they waved good-bye, signaling that everything was all right.

In the churchyard the children met the verger. Sami handed him the letter. The old man read it in silence, then weighed it up and down in his hand as if deciding

43

what to do with it and the five children standing in front of him.

"We wanted you to take the letter to the priest," said Sami.

"All right," said the verger. "I'll give it to him. But you must wait here because at the moment he's saying Mass. Stay here until I come back."

The children clustered nervously around Abrasza. "Have you ever spoken to a priest before?" one of them asked.

"No," said Abrasza.

"I'm frightened," said Zygmunt. "I think we had better go back home."

Aronek, who had stationed himself near the gate, ran up. "Germans coming," he said. By then the children could hear the boots of an SS squad in the street.

The only place to hide was in the church. The children rushed up to the great doors, and Abrasza opened one enough for them to slip through. It was the first time that any of the children had ever been in a church, and they were astounded at the size of the building, its statues, the quiet. The parishioners were on their knees, lips moving in silent prayer, with the tinkle of bells repeated at intervals.

The children clustered by the poor box, afraid to move or even to breathe loudly. Then Hanka made a discovery which she whispered to Sami. All the people in the church were wearing white armlets with a blue Star of David. They were meshummadim: converted Jews. Many came from families which had been Catholic for two or three generations. Some were unaware of their origins until the Germans discovered they had a Jewish ancestor, which was enough to rob them of Aryan standing. Others were among the Jews who became converts to Christianity as the Nazi tide started to flood Europe.

The priest, Father Godlefsky, wore an armlet. The son of a rich Jewish shopkeeper, he had run away from home at thirteen and was baptized. He studied, took holy orders, and became a priest. The service ended and the worshipers filed by the staring children. Then the verger gave their note to the priest, and he slowly walked to them. He gave them a friendly nod, then said they could play in the churchyard as long as they did not make noise.

"But," he warned, "I fear the favor will not be granted for long. They tell me the church will soon be excluded from the ghetto, and I may no longer be here."

On the following Saturday Sami and the others found Father Godlefsky's prediction had already come true. When the children approached the church they found Jewish workmen with armed guards setting up a barbed-wire barricade, making a new ghetto boundary. At the same time, other gangs of workmen were starting to build a wall which would take the place of the temporary barricade. The church was now outside the ghetto limits. The stone crosses had been destroyed, and the church itself was being gutted and converted into a warehouse for ordinance supplies. The priest and his parishioners had been "resettled to the East."

"The walls are closing in on us," Korczak told Mrs. Stefa that night. But the walls had been closing in on the Jews in the ghetto since the first few months of 1939, when impoverished Jewish refugees from Germany began pouring into Poland, wandering from house to house peddling hosiery, ties, and handkerchiefs. The controlled German press, which had been conducting a violent campaign of hatred against Poland, was demanding the Polish Corridor and Upper Silesia. England and France had guaranteed the Polish borders, but the Polish newspapers were hinting that the Polish Army was not in a state of preparedness.

In the parks and squares of Warsaw, trenches had been dug to serve as shelters against a possible bombardment of the city. United in the face of danger, priests and rabbis turned the first spade of earth. Substantial citizens, Christians and Jews, volunteered to help with the digging. Because of the fear of a sudden attack by German planes, the work went on at night. All windows were hung with blankets or black sheets of paper. The Polish Army was partly mobilized, but the generals and colonels who had ruled the country ever since the Pilsudski uprising were far from prepared for a modern war. For all Marshal Smigly Rydz's assurances that every inch of Polish soil would be defended, it was expected that the Polish forces would only try to hold a line along the River Bug.

In June of 1939 there was a violent outbreak of anti-Semitism in Warsaw. While leading the children through the streets of Warsaw one day Korczak was struck, a terrible experience for him as well as for the children forced to witness his humiliation. Weeks later he went with the children and a woman supervisor on a trip to the suburban village of Swider. It was a hot summer day, ideal for bathing, and the children rushed to the stream that skirted the village. While they were in the water the woman supervisor paced the bank nervously, fearing a child might drown.

"Don't let it worry you," he said wearily. "Perhaps that is the best thing that could happen to a Jewish orphan."

Next door to Krochmalna 92, the location of Korczak's orphanage at this time, there was a home for Polish boys who now attacked the Jewish children and called them "Dirty Jews" whenever they saw them. It got so bad that some of the younger children were afraid to go out alone. Korczak finally paid a visit to the director of the neighboring orphanage to complain, and he too was reviled and insulted.

At dawn on September 1, without declaration of war, German planes bombed Polish airfields and German troops crossed Poland's frontiers from the west, from East Prussia, and from Slovakia. Less than a week later the Polish government fled the capital. On September 25 the Warsaw command rejected a summons to capitulate and the Luftwaffe and German artillery began to systematically demolish the city.

Korczak was asked to deliver morale-building talks over radio Warsaw during the siege. He spoke beautifully and passionately, calling on the city and the nation to continue its resistance. He kept speaking over the radio until the station was silenced by a direct hit.

At the height of the bombing he went into the streets to see if he could be of help as a doctor. He found a dying soldier lying untended in a gutter and tugged and

47

carried the man to a brothel on Krochmalna Street so he could at least die under a roof. The madame refused him entrance, and the bleeding man, in Korczak's arms, died within minutes on the steps.

Korczak gathered as many homeless children as he could handle and brought them to the orphanage. The building, though in an area of heavy bombing, was still comparatively undamaged, but all of the windows on the second floor had been shattered and some flooring had been torn up. During the air raids the children had been herded into the kitchen on the ground floor; the windows had been closed up with sandbags. There had been only one casualty: nine-year-old Joseph Stockman had died of exhaustion and pneumonia after attempting to put out a fire started by an incendiary bomb.

Korczak did his best to maintain a measure of calm in the orphanage. One evening while the children were having dinner there was a tremendous explosion nearby. The screaming children flung themselves under the dining-room tables. During the first lull in the attack Korczak said he was going to have a look at the damage caused by the bomb that had exploded so near the house. Samy Gogol followed him outside.

There was a large bomb crater in the front yard. Korczak walked carefully over to inspect it. To his amazement he saw his own hat lying in the hole. The concusion had somehow sucked it through a window. Korczak turned to Samy with a large smile on his face.

"I think I see a message for me here, Samy," he said. "From now on I had better wear my hat all the time. The

Germans saw my bald head and they want to cover it. That's why the bomb."

Samy clambered into the crater and rescued the hat. When he returned to the dining room with Korczak the children were still cowering under the tables, whimpering with fright. "We can continue to eat," Korczak announced. "The Germans merely dug a hole in the front yard so we could plant another tree."

When the Warsaw garrison surrendered on September 27, Korczak issued an appeal addressed to the citizens of the area around Krochmalna 92. It read:

> We have repelled two attempts at pogrom and three of pillage and rape. My concern is for the Orphans' Home. We cannot perish. . . . I have survived three revolutions and this is my fourth war. Only the weak, the debased and dishonorable collapse in the face of temporary misfortune. Our patrons do not exist any longer. Some of them have been killed; others face economic ruin. Some deserted; others acted egotistically. . . . Children are our future. They are the defenders of our future. I demand money. One hundred zlotys for the fund of the Orphans' Home from all of you. I will come and collect the money personally within the next few days, and I cannot take "No" for an answer.

There were many responses to his appeal. One of Warsaw's biggest chocolate factories, Weggel, gave a large amount of money. Some of the smaller stores contributed, and there were many private donations.

On October 1 German troops entered Warsaw. Three days later Polish engineer Adam Czerniakow was called to Gestapo Headquarters at Szucha Avenue. Before the war Czerniakow had been a little-known leader in the

Artisan's Union. Politically he considered himself a Zionist, although he never played an important role in Jewish life. He spoke Polish exclusively, which in the Jewish community was a mark of assimilationist tendencies.

The Germans ordered Czerniakow to appoint a new Jewish Council, which they christened the Judenrat, to supplant the Jewish Community Council which had been the traditional authority in the religious life of the Jews. But the new organization was to be a racial institution, not religious; it was to be a government responsible for all Jews in Warsaw but without a trace of independence. It was the Judenrat's duty to furnish the work battalions demanded by the Germans; to maintain law and order through an Ordnungsdienst consisting of Jewish policemen; to train workers in needed skills; to attend to sanitation and medical needs; and to levy taxes.

By December Dr. Hans Franck, Governor General of Poland, announced that the Poles did not need universities or secondary schools. "The Polish land is to be changed into an intellectual desert," he said. The Germans were determined that the next generation in Poland would have only two types of people: the uneducated and the Germanized.

Dr. Franck ordered that all textbooks of history and geography be confiscated, along with children's readers. Children were to be taught to read without using books; all instruction was to be in German, and students must learn to "know and like" the German language. The music of Chopin was forbidden. Poles were not to mingle socially with Germans, and they were allowed no cultural

50

activities; there were, however, many new bars opened where liquor was inexpensive.

Jewish literature and all books in English were confiscated and burned. More than fifteen hundred authors were eliminated from the nation's libraries. A monument to Adam Mickiwicz, Poland's greatest poet, was demolished at Cracow. Korczak's books, too, were banned, but he managed to send a few copies to the orphanage at Bielany where they were hidden in a wall which was then replastered.

Korczak had correctly anticipated the Polish antiSemitism which blossomed in the wake of the Nazi occupation, but he simply redoubled his efforts to keep the orphanage running as usual. He had to devote more time than ever to begging, and with apparent disregard for the Germans he trudged the streets of the war-ravaged city, dressed in his old uniform of a Polish Army officer, minus the epaulets.

A friend of Korczak's, Hindah Levi Lisner, recalled how he looked in those days. "The uniform was old and tattered. He did not look much like a Polish officer with his short beard, bald head, and stooped walk. But he did have a kind of whimsical glory in his appearance."

The uniform may have saved him from some harassment, but it complicated his work once. He was visiting an old Jewish lady who owned a large shoe-polish factory in Warsaw. When he asked her for money, she said, "What orphanage did you say? I can't hear you too well. I'm a little deaf, you know. Is it a Catholic orphanage?"

"No," shouted Korczak.

"Protestant?" she asked.

"No," roared Korczak. "It's Jewish."

"What?" said the old lady. "What is a Polish Army officer doing collecting money for a Jewish orphanage in a city under German occupation?"

"I run the orphanage," he shouted into her ear.

The lady shook her head and ordered him to turn around. Then she lifted up her several skirts, extracted a roll of bank notes, and gave them to him.

Before cold weather set in he managed to stock the orphanage cellar with coal, potatoes, flour, enough to weather another winter. He had even begged the services of a glazier who repaired the blown-in windows at cost and a carpenter who donated the wood and time to repair the damaged floors.

When the severe winter ended and spring made its first tentative appearance, the German grip tightened. Jews were rounded up in the streets and beaten or sent to work battalions from which few ever returned. Teen-age boys were seized from playgrounds and the street and sent to work in Germany. As they arrived at school, youngsters would be packed into waiting lorries and taken off to labor in quarries and roads. And children witnessed terrible scenes; they saw brutal beatings, mass executions, the corpses of "saboteurs" exposed on gallows made in the shape of a swastika.

The Germans introduced a special bread, clayish and poisonous, for the Jews, rationed in quantities far from sufficient to feed those who depended on it. More ominous was the brick wall being constructed on the fringes of the Jewish quarters by Jewish laborers with German overseers, guns and whips in hand. The Polish newspapers were no longer subtle in encouraging hatred for the Jews, and bloody pogroms carried out by street gangs of young toughs were encouraged by the Germans and tolerated by the Poles.

Learning of the situation in Poland, friends of Korczak in Palestine urgently pleaded with him to join them. The Germans still allowed Polish Jews to emigrate to Palestine in exchange for a large fee. He considered the matter carefully, knowing that this might be his last chance to leave Poland. But his feeling of responsibility for the welfare of his children took precedence over his desire to end his days in peace and study.

In December 1939 he answered the invitation, writing:

It would be risking the bankruptcy of my ideals, from which there would be no recovery, were I to go to Palestine and leave all that is dear to me behind. Would I be able to look into another pair of child's eyes? Could I just shake it all off. . . ?

To disappoint and undermine the confidence of the children would be to inflict a wound.

Just now I have an irrepressible desire to visit little towns here, just as I visited kibbutzim in Palestine. Perhaps I can say something that would ease the burden of many; lift a load from shoulders that are too small to carry one more ounce. . . .

I feel responsible for the monumental work I have started and for the cause I have served for over thirty years. I have tied my life and myself to it with complicated knots, and I don't think anything but death can untie them. I feel responsible for many young lives. Not because I would leave the world around me in turmoil, but because I could not defend from afar the rights of the child.

Friends of Miss Stefa, too, wrote asking her to return. In January 1940, Fega Lipschitz, who was at Kibbutz Eyn Harod, managed to send a message to Stefa through the Red Cross saying arrangements had been made to bring her to Palestine. In March Stefa answered: "My dear, we are all right. I am working in the Orphan's Home a little and Korczak a lot. I haven't come because I don't want to go without my children. Yours, Stefa."

Within the month, the Germans stopped issuing emigration permits. The Jews of Warsaw were trapped.

In the spring of 1940 Korczak asked Hanna Mortkowicz-Olczakowa, daughter of his publisher, to visit with him to discuss the production of a school banner. He had been thinking of the project for a long time, and he wanted to be certain the design and colors were right. One side of the banner was to be green and against this green background, a design of chestnut flowers, the symbol of eternal blossoming. The reverse side of the banner was to be white with a blue Star of David.

The banner was to be given to the children at the Jewish cemetery during a ceremony commemorating the two orphans who had died at the Home: Esther Weintraub, who died of typhus during World War I while Korczak was away, and Joseph Stockman, who died during the siege of Warsaw. Mrs. Olczakowa recalls that Korczak and Stefa were standing in his office-bedroom, looking at portraits of the two children.

"Korczak was looking at them in a sort of stupor and did not even notice my entrance. He stood like a grief-stricken father who had just received news of the death of his children. Out of thousands of orphans he had

54

looked after and brought up in his homes only two had died. His eyes were filled with tears and his face reflected the deepest pain. Finally he emerged from his reverie of grief and looked up. Then he smiled sorrowfully.

" 'It is true,' he said, as if he had heard my thoughts. 'Only two have died.' "

On Friday morning, June 26, 1940, the B.B.C. broadcast a report about the fate of Polish Jewry. They told about the cruelties perpetrated at Slonim, Vilna, Lemberg, Chelmno, and Belzec; according to reports 700,000 Jews had been killed. The broadcast vowed revenge and a final accounting for all the deeds of violence. The German-controlled press maintained a complete silence about the sensational accusations. The Warsaw Jews believed this was a good sign, feeling that since the spotlight had been focused on them, the Germans would be afraid to perpetrate new massacres. Stories were told that Jews, after deportation from Ostrowiecz in sealed wagons, had been set free.

The Jews maintained their optimism until October 14, 1940, when the network of loudspeakers set up by the Germans throughout the city blared the order that all Jews were to be resettled in one district of the town. Notices were posted on the walls of buildings giving the Jews two weeks to comply with the order. The final date was later postponed two more weeks, until November 11.

The order meant that 400,000 Jews would be squeezed into a ghetto of 1,359 apartment houses. Large families counted themselves fortunate to find one room; tens of thousands lived in wet cellars, stair landings, courtyards, or the streets themselves.

55

Korczak saw with despair that Krochmalna Street was in the Aryan section: the orphanage would have to move.

On November 10 Korczak was called from a classroom by Stefa.

"An SS officer and a man from the Gestapo are in your office," she said, eyes wide with fear.

Without bothering to change from his faded green smock he hurried to his office. The SS officer was tall, with cold, blue eyes and close-cropped gray hair. He seemed to be in his fifties.

"I am Dr. Scugart," he said in Polish.

The other man said nothing. He, too, was about fifty years old. His impassive face, dark-eyed, thin-lipped, struck Korczak as devoid of any human emotions, even hatred.

"Do you speak German?" Dr. Scugart asked.

For a moment Korczak considered saying he did not, thus forcing the interview to be conducted through a translator, which would give him a chance to consider his answers carefully. But he decided that the Gestapo man probably knew from his dossier that he could speak German.

"Ich kann ein bisschen Deutsch sprechen," he answered.

Dr. Scugart smiled. The other man, who had been pacing up and down in the small room stopped in front of the battered bookcase. "What's this? Don't you know Jews are not supposed to have libraries?" he asked in Polish with a heavy Poznan accent.

"Those are just the records of the institution, certificates, and some research notes—all in my handwriting," Korczak answered.

56

"I am a doctor myself," Scugart said. "Before the war I was a surgeon. Now I am in uniform, but once a doctor, always a doctor, as you know. You are a pediatrician but you were in the Army, eh?"

He paused, and Korczak nodded.

"That is why I have been chosen to execute the orders given by the authorities. You are to vacate this house, which is needed for our troops. It is a nice place, better than most in this city."

"But the house is destroyed now," Korczak said. "Many of the windows do not have glass. There is no central heating. The walls are dirty. The sewers are broken. There is no gas for cooking and the building . . ."

Scugart cut him off: "You Jewish dreamers!" he said. "Hygiene is not necessary for German soldiers. You Jews think that you must live in comfortable surroundings with plenty of food to eat. We Germans know that in order to conquer the world we must be hungry. And while you may conquer the next world, we will conquer this one."

The Gestapo man smiled thinly.

"Inside the ghetto you will be much better off," Scugart continued. "You will be safe. There is always a risk that this house will be attacked by Polish mobs here."

"But where will we go?" asked Korczak.

"That is your problem. If you can't find a solution, perhaps we will have to help you."

The menace underlying Scugart's words was not lost on Korczak. Nevertheless, he had one question he felt he must ask: "Why do you punish the small children?"

"The small Jew will grow up into a big Jew someday,"

said Scugart. "Our New Order must have a firm foundation."

The other man, who had been sitting quietly during the exchange, said something rapidly in what sounded like a German dialect. Scugart nodded and, impatience in his voice, said to Korczak, "That's enough discussion. If you have any problems you come to me from now on. I am in charge of this section."

"I am happy that a doctor is in charge of children's cases," Korczak said with irony.

"Very well," Scugart said. "Then let's start our collaboration by having this house empty—tomorrow."

"That's impossible," Korczak exclaimed, "I can't find . . ."

"An order is an order," said Scugart. "Everything is to be left behind. No one is allowed to take anything except personal effects and one change of clothing. I hope you will not force me to search your children. Heil Hitler!"

Stefa, who had been standing in the hallway waiting for the men to leave, came rushing in. When he explained the situation to her she was unable to comprehend it. "Where will we go?" she wailed.

"We have to ask the children what to do about it," he said.

"Stop joking," said Stefa. "What will they know about it?"

"We have to let them know everything, discuss it with them. We must call a meeting of the older children, and then we must all go out over the city at once to see what we can find. We must have another place before tomorrow."

After a discussion with the older children he went to the Judenrat offices. They arranged for Korczak to take over a building which had been occupied by the Technical College of Roesslers at Chlodna 33, which was within the ghetto boundaries. The orphanage would share the building with ten or twelve families: the orphanage on the left, and the other families on the right side of the courtyard. Korczak's old friend, Myron Zylberberg, who taught the children Hebrew, lived with his wife in a room on the first floor.

Hanna Mortkowicz-Olczakowa, daughter of his publisher, saw Korczak soon after the move had been arranged. He confided to her a plan to move the orphanage as if he were transferring a large theatrical troupe and was doing it as an advertisement for a show he was staging. He proposed a street parade in which a long line of children would march with lamps, paintings, bedding, cages containing their pet birds and animals.

His biggest problem was how to transfer the sick children. He feared the Germans might simply murder them. Finally he decided that the larger boys and girls would carry the sick children on their backs, pickaback style, as part of the show.

The move was accomplished without incident. However, when the last barrow he hired from the black marketeers, Kohn and Heller, was being trundled out of the gates loaded with potatoes, the German soldier in charge of overseeing the move confiscated it.

Korczak in his old uniform, started yelling in German at the soldier who automatically jumped to attention.

But after a moment he demanded to know if Korczak was a Jew.

"Yes, I am."

"Then why aren't you wearing the armband?"

"I fought in four wars, four revolutions. I didn't wear an armband before so why should I wear one now?"

"And why do you still wear the uniform?" asked the soldier angrily.

"The one who gave me the order to wear it didn't give me the order to take it off," said Korczak.

"You are under arrest," snapped the German.

"If you are going to take me to Gestapo Headquarters, don't bother," said Korczak "I'll go myself."

Korczak immediately went to Gestapo Headquarters on Szucha Avenue to demand the release of his potatoes. A barbed-wire entanglement kept passersby from getting near the building but Korczak marched through the gate as the sentries in guard boxes snapped to attention. Once inside he demanded to see Obersturmfuehrer Brandt, Chief of Police of the Warsaw District. The guard, impressed by the uniform, admitted him to the basement corridor where Brandt had a temporary office.

Korczak had second thoughts as he walked down the corridor and saw the four collective cells called trams by the prisoners, rooms in which prisoners awaiting interrogation sat on benches facing the wall, with guards who would whip them for turning around or talking.

Brandt's office was small; there was only an oak desk with a gooseneck lamp and a smaller desk holding an Adler typewriter for a secretary. There was a clothes rack on which Brandt had hung his green uniform coat, cap, and holstered service pistol. By the door was a stool across which lay a menacing whip used to assist interrogations. There was a window at one end of the office through which the barrel of a machine pistol was pointed menacingly at visitors. The face of the soldier holding the gun was dimly visible.

Without glancing up from his papers at his visitor, Brandt asked if he could be of service.

"Yes, you can," said Korczak. "Your men confiscated a wagonload of potatoes destined for my children."

"A wagonload!" said Brandt. "How many children do you have?"

"Two hundred," said Korczak.

Brandt examined Korczak with interest, the broad face and small clever eyes showing some interest. "My compliments," he said. "Two hundred!"

"They are children in my orphanage," explained Korczak.

Brandt motioned Korczak to sit on the stool. Korczak carefully removed the whip and sat down.

"On what front did you fight?" asked Brandt.

"I wasn't wanted in this war," said Korczak. "But I was useful in the Russian-Japanese War and in the First World War. The Medical Corps. I am a doctor and the head of an orphanage."

"And where is the orphanage?"

"As of today—at Chlodna 33."

Brandt walked to a huge map of Warsaw on the wall then turned around, his eyes incredulous. "Your orphanage is in the ghetto?" he asked.

"Unfortunately, yes."

"You. A Polish officer. What are you doing in the ghetto?"

"I was moved there by your men."

Suddenly Brandt's attitude changed. "You are a Jew," he said, making a statement rather than asking a question. "And where is your armband?"

"I told you, I am a doctor," said Korczak. "If I wear the armband I might be picked up for labor service, and I must stay with my children."

Brandt, speaking in a normal voice into a microphone hidden someplace, asked the guard to come in. The guard unceremoniously jabbed his pistol into Korczak's back and marched him to an isolation cell which was farther along the basement corridor. The cell was about the width of his outstretched arms and a little longer than the cot it contained. There was one light bulb in the ceiling which was always kept lit, and a small barred window which let in neither light nor air. The door had a Judas hole through which guards peered every quarter of an hour. There was no toilet other than a bucket, and on the wall there was an ominous inscription in Polish: "Oh Lord, how they do beat!" The inscription was superfluous. He heard the sound of screams, moaning, and whipping every hour of the next two days.

On the morning of the third day he was sent with twenty-six other prisoners—lucky ones who had survived interrogation—to the notorious Pawiak Prison which was reserved for the most dangerous criminals.

In Korczak's new cell he had companions: a Jewish worker named Leib, a young Polish priest, a Polish railway man accused of murder, two smugglers, and an old

Jew who had also been arrested for not wearing an armband.

Korczak asked the old man with his caftan and side curls why—since he was so obviously a Jew—he did not wear the band. The old man smiled and combed his fingers through his lank gray beard. "There are human laws, unstable and transitory," he said in Talmudic tones. "And there are the laws of God which are eternal. I believe and obey only God's laws."

Korczak had nothing in common with the man except that they were both hated as Jews. They were, in the eyes of the German conqueror, alike. And though he was annoyed by the old man's bizarre appearance and his calmly superior attitude, they soon became friendly enough to get embroiled in arguments which helped pass the time.

Korczak was imprisoned for four months before three of his former pupils, Benjamin Cukier, Harry Kaliszer, and Chaim Buraztyn, collected from the Jewish community the three thousand zlotys required for his release. On the day he left the prison the old Jew spoke to him for the last time.

"Be advised by an old man," he said. "It is not practicable to fight the Germans. It will only do you harm. Why puff yourself up and take a place in the sun? It is not good for a Jew to set himself where everybody can see him. A Jew is much better off in the shadow."

Korczak sneered to himself. "What a coward he is. These stupid, old-fashioned attitudes. Oh, yes, only keep the Christians from noticing you. Not I—in the broad light of day I will look every man straight in the eye."

Back in the orphanage the children clustered around him as though he were a hero, asking what it was like in Pawiak. "It was very interesting to be in there," he said. "The same stories I tell you I told the murderers and thieves. And they were as happy with the stories as you are. They were sorry to see me go. Now who is going to tell them stories?"

"Why did you scream at the Germans when they took the potatoes?" asked Samy Gogol.

Korczak smiled. "If you scream at the Germans they think you are in authority. Maybe I made a mistake this time."

Week by week the ghetto grew smaller; as sections were evacuated the wall was tightened around the remaining area like a noose.

Then, with the completion of deportations from Lodz, the next largest ghetto, Warsaw's doom came nearer. The ghetto was to be slowly strangled. In December 1941, Warsaw Jews were forbidden to receive food packages. Communications through the mail or telephone with the outside world were completely cut off. Korczak's last telephone call was to the Doctor Grzegorzewska. He asked her to contact one of his former pupils, Wawrzykowski, to ask about a promised supply of vegetables and potatoes.

Maria Czapska, a Gentile friend of Korczak, managed to enter the ghetto on a borrowed worker's pass. It was a wet, dreary day. The streets, covered with mud and snow, were crowded with people, hurrying in all directions, carrying bundles, pushing carts or sleds. Beggars stretched out on the dirty snow, exposing their emaciated limbs, purple with cold. Passersby were assailed by throngs of ragged children, clothes held together by string, brown eyes staring, begging for food. The adults were indifferent to their pleas: everyone had his mind on only one thought—his own survival.

Mrs. Czapska brought a present for Korczak: a packet of coffee grounds to which were added some fresh beans contributed from a Portuguese friend who sent regular parcels to be smuggled into the ghetto. She found the doctor seated at his desk, surrounded by children who had come to exchange books. The serene atmosphere was a complete contrast to the madness and pain in the streets just outside the door.

"What is the children's reaction to the new quarters?" Mrs. Czapska asked.

"They have not suffered too much," he said. "They have plenty to keep them occupied. They are busy now preparing a show for the holidays, and that's all they are interested in for the moment."

"And you, Doctor?" she asked. "How do you feel?"

"Like a butterfly about to leave its chrysalis. A butterfly that will soon spread out its wings and fly. I know that I am about to enter a better world—I can almost feel it . . ." Then, with his old smile, he added, "But perhaps it is only arteriosclerosis."

When they parted he said simply, "Thank you. Thank you for not trying to persuade me to abandon this purgatory."

He was so obsessed by his feeling of responsibility for the children in his orphanage that in his dealings with officials of the community's welfare groups he no longer requested assistance; he demanded it. He besieged the offices of the Jewish Communal Council and CENTOS, the Jewish Assistance Committee. Despite German orders that individuals must not solicit donations on their own, he begged everywhere and did not hesitate to call on collaborators like Kohn and Heller. A copy of a letter sent to a madame of a brothel still survives. The tone is curious for a man who was begging:

"For the cynical attempt to shift the responsibility for the care of orphans onto the shoulders of the general public, for the shameless insults and curses when the attempt did not succeed, you are ordered to pay the sum of five hundred zlotys within five days to the 'Help The Orphans' fund. The sum is a small one, because of the low character of the district and the house you frequent."

Even his sister Anna complained in a letter that he had time to "make calls" but not to visit her. In a reply he explained:

I do not make calls. I go begging for money and food-stuffs, information, and assistance. If that is what you mean by calls, it is a hard and humiliating work. And one must be able to make jokes, for people are tired of seeing long faces.

I often go to the Chmielarz family. They pretty well keep me in food. These are not calls. I am sure they do it out of compassion. They say, however, it is an exchange of favors. All the same, they are amiable, obliging, and soothing.

Relaxation by reading is beginning to help me. An unpleasant discovery: I am mad, and that worries me.

I endeavor to carry out my obligations within my mental capacity provided they are possible of being fulfilled with

the means at my disposal. I have never refused to do anything that was within my power. But I never felt bound to
assist the functionaries. They help themselves. Your re-
proach is unjustified.

Actually the majority of the children under Korczak's
care were not orphans in the strict sense of the word. Most
had at least one living parent or relative, but their families
were unable to feed or care for them properly.

Korczak's children survived on a daily diet of a slice of
bread with beetroot marmalade plus a small bowl of
shredded cabbage and a boiled potato. Occasionally this
would be supplemented by groats mixed with horsemeat
or horse's blood. On very special occasions a kind of cake
was made with flour. Yet meager as the orphanage rations
were, they were better than those of the average ghetto
family. Parents and relatives constantly besieged Korczak
to take in their children and he spent hours every day
investigating such cases.

Nussen Faynar was typical. One day Korczak went to
Milna Street 64, where he had heard that two children,
of the Faynar family were starving. As he walked through
the courtyard he saw an emaciated, six-year-old boy playing listlessly with a bottle cap in the yard. He asked the
child where the Faynar family lived. The boy was Nussen
Faynar, and his parents had been dead for six weeks. The
father died of starvation on a Friday. All that night and
Saturday the mother waited for the burial detail. When it
finally came she said, "Oh, you are here at last." Then she
died.

The boy and his sister were left to depend on the
charity of relatives. "My sister Hanka takes care of us,"

Nussen explained. Korczak remembered Hanka as a dark-eyed, dark-haired little girl whose grandmother lived at Krochmalna 72. In better days the children's aunt had made contributions to the orphanage.

Korczak arranged for fourteen-year-old Hanka to bring her brother to the orphanage. On the morning they arrived it was pouring rain. The children were soaking wet in their thin clothes. Hanka was carrying a cardboard suitcase which was soggy from the rain.

"Are you crazy to come out in such weather?" Korczak asked her.

"I was afraid I would lose the place for my brother," said Hanka, who was half-carrying Nussen.

Korczak lifted Nussen tenderly up in his arms and brought him to the isolation ward. He told Hanka she could come see her brother every day but she would not be allowed into the room. Instead he would place a chair outside so they could visit. Since medicines were not obtainable for sick children, Nussen's only treatment was rest and some precious cod-liver oil.

When he finally was well Nussen told Hanka that Korczak had taught him how to play chess while he was sick. He also marveled at the old man's stamina. "He never sleeps. He either reads or writes or takes care of us children all day long. All he eats is tea and bread."

Unlike most of the children in the orphanage, Nussen was an Orthodox Jew. When he was well enough to get up for services and pray in the mornings, Korczak gave him an alarm clock.

"If you want to pray, get up at six instead of seven," the doctor cautioned. "But the moment the alarm rings, stop

68

it so the other children aren't awakened. They need every moment of sleep they can get."

It was rare for the children to have restful nights. Through the broken windows they heard the cries of the hungry and dying, the pounding footsteps of patrols, occasional shots. And their sleep was disturbed by their own feverish dreams. Korczak was fighting a losing battle trying to keep his brood healthy. But at least there had been no cases of typhus among them, although the dread disease was everywhere in the ghetto.

Although the terrible world was kept outside, Korczak knew he was fighting a losing battle. The children were constantly hungry. To further complicate matters there was an outbreak of diarrhea and vomiting. In one night alone the boys lost eighty kilograms, he noted in his little book: one kilo per boy. The girls lost a shade less.

He blamed the outbreak on a stew to which had been added some eggs, in the hope of improving the flavor, that were not quite fresh. He had to treat the emergency in total darkness. The children vomited, groaned, and wept. The only medicine available was as much precipitated chalk as they could choke down to stop the diarrhea.

The orphanage had become a sanitarium for querulous children concerned with their health. The morning talk was "What's your temperature?" Breakfast discussion was about how ill one felt and how well one slept. The children crawled around slowly. Only their skin was normal, Korczak wrote, and under it brooded apathy, fatigue, wrath, rebellion, longing, and loneliness. Their diaries were full of painful awareness of the seriousness of their situation and their trust in Korczak.

☆ 5 ☆

Excerpt from the Minutes of the Children's Court, June 1942. Signed, Natalia Poz, Recording Secretary.

Judges: Jacob, Chaim, Bula, Jankiel, Hannia

3rd Case. Schmulik was before the Court on a charge of Mrs. Stefa that he wasted the equivalent of three potatoes while on kitchen duty by not peeling them properly. His excuse: "He was in a hurry to go out and play." As a result of his action the Thursday night soup was thin. Unanimous judgment: (Para. 13) The Court regrets that the thing happened, but it was not the fault

70

of Schmulik who was too young to be able to foresee the consequence of his action.

12th Case. Janek and Irene have made a complaint against Musik, charging him with destroying their sand castle. When told he was to be brought before the Court, Musik said, "I don't care." Musik has said he does not like the Court and believes if he is to be punished he should be hit. He prefers to do what he wants and be punished for it then, rather than appear in Court.

Two judges contend Musik should be discharged from the orphanage because he is undermining the authority of the Court and system (Para. 1,000). The other three favor (Para. 800): For one week from this date Musik is to be excluded from his rights to the Court. Therefore, he cannot bring anyone to Court and he has no rights. Anyone can treat him as they wish without fear of being brought before the Court.

The keystone of Korczak's educational system was the Children's Court of Honor. He had written the code of behavior in 1914 in Jerornia while serving in the Russian Army. It expressed the spirit which governed the lives of the orphans in his care.

If someone has done something bad it is best to forgive him. If he did something bad because he did not know, then he knows now. If he had done something bad unintentionally, he will be more careful in the future. If he does something bad because he finds it hard to adjust, he will now make an effort. If he had done something bad at the instigation of others, then he will no longer listen to them.

71

If someone does something bad, it is best to forgive and to wait until he reforms.

But the court must defend the meek from the annoyances of the strong; the court must defend the conscientious and industrious from the disturbances of the slack and indolent; the court must maintain order, because disorder injures the good, meek, and conscientious people.

A court does not personify justice but should strive for justice. A court is not truth but desires truth.

Judges may err. Judges may punish for acts they themselves commit. They may say that the things they themselves do are bad.

But the judge who knowingly passes a dishonest sentence, covers himself with dishonor.

The Court met every Saturday. The sessions, attended by everyone in the orphanage, were held in the dining room. Chairs and tables were pushed back against the wall, and one table, covered with a green cloth, became the judge's bench. There were five judges, chosen by lot from those children who did not have court cases pending themselves during the week. The only adult on the board was the secretary, most often Korczak or Mrs. Stefa.

Before the Court was called to order, Korczak always asked: "No one has been hit by the staff? True or not?" In his mind the striking of a child by an adult was the most serious crime of all and was not to be tolerated. He believed that if a child did anything wrong, he was to be called before the Court and the punishment, if required, meted out fairly and not administered in a flush of anger. There is no record of any adult having struck a child in one of Korczak's orphanages.

72

Complaints were read aloud. The judges asked the defendant if the complaint was true or not. The words guilty or not guilty were never used, as Korczak did not like to use such words in dealing with children.

Every possible situation which could arise between children had been codified and classified by him into one thousand paragraphs. It was the responsibility of the judges to find the proper paragraph to fit the case. The first hundred paragraphs, for example, excused the child as innocent or said the Court would not take the case under consideration.

Paragraphs 100 to 700 called for such minor punishments as the withholding of dessert for a week or an order to the offender to apologize for wrongdoing and promise not to repeat the offense.

From Paragraphs 700 to 1,000 the punishments were increasingly harsh. Paragraph 700 called for the child's relatives, if any lived, to be notified of his misdeed.

Paragraph 900 called for the miscreant to find another child who would agree to be his supervisor during a three-month probation period. Any punishments incurred during that time would be given to the supervisor. If the punished child was unable to find an older sponsor, he was expelled from the orphanage.

Paragraph 1,000 ordered expulsion from the orphanage. It was invoked only twice in twenty-five years.

The Court's decision was reached by majority vote and was subject to appeal to Korczak after one month. All verdicts were published in the Court *Gazette*.

During the first year of the Court at Our Home more than 3,500 cases were brought before it and 25 issues of the Court *Gazette* were published. Complaints were made orally. Korczak soon discovered that many of the small things that irritate and distress children would not otherwise come to the attention of an adult or parent. Through the Court he was kept in better touch with all areas of the children's lives, but the number of cases was too great. In an attempt to reduce the number of trivial charges he finally ruled that all complaints be put in writing, signed, and dropped in a complaint box.

The Court also functioned at the orphanage at Bielany and at the summer camp. In the course of two summers at camp there were forty-three cases. Considering that two children playing in one room can quarrel five times within an hour, tell their mother, make up, and quarrel again, the number of cases is not exorbitant for 150 boys living in the country for four weeks and another 120 boys for four more weeks. One trial record has survived:

July 3, 1928, Friday after tea, the camp Court composed of the following judges: Tarkowski of Group A. Holtz of Group B, Antczak of Group C, Faszczewski of Group D, and Spychalski of Group E, reviewed the case of the destruction of a bird's nest by P., S., and B.

P. the elder, S., and B. destroyed a bird's nest. There were five eggs in the nest. The boys took the nest apart and counted that it was made of 73 feathers, 280 straws, 246 bits of birch bark, 148 horse hairs. This enormous labor of the tiny, frail bird was wasted. And the little eggs were the bird's children. The home was ruined and the children killed.

Your honors, look at the defendants. One is crying, another is sitting dejectedly, and the third is smiling in order to hide his sorrow. Your honors, would they have committed this evil and stupid deed if they had known then what they know now?

I assure you that if the little bird were here in Court and could speak to you, it would say: "The boys have done a very great wrong but forgive them because punishment will neither give us back our home nor restore the children to us. Ask them never to do this again because we too have hearts, capable of love and forgiveness." Your honors, you must not be worse than the little bird.

The Court rules: S. and B. confessed voluntarily.

1. A nest was destroyed for the first time.

2. This was not done with evil intentions, not to harm a defenseless and innocent little bird.

3. The defendants did not give any excuses, did not lie but admitted everything right away.

Taking this into consideration, the Court rules:

B. and P. the elder will eat their supper alone tonight.

Furthermore, considering that the part of S. in the destruction of the nest was not proved and seeing his true remorse, the Court rules:

Forgive S. . . .

Although Korczak usually relied on the Court to handle disciplinary problems he sometimes took matters into his own hands. One of the few children in orphanage history to get a judgment of Paragraph 900 was Israel Shmuel Zyngman.

Shmuel arrived at Our Home in 1928 at the age of eight. His father had died two years earlier. The eldest of three children, Shmuel was on the street in Praga, a Warsaw suburb, almost twenty-four hours a day and showed every sign of becoming a delinquent child. His mother pleaded for him to be accepted at the orphanage.

Shmuel was very undernourished and Korczak arranged for him to have a special diet to avoid the all-too-common tuberculosis. When Shmuel was playing with other children on the shady side of the yard Korczak would come out of the house and pickaback him into the sun.

Because Shmuel came from an Orthodox Jewish family he was sent to a Yiddish school, unlike the other children who attended Government School No. 90 which was only a short distance away. Shmuel's school was farther but he left at the same time as the others and was frequently late. Then he was given money to take a tram every day, but he still arrived late.

Two older orthodox boys came to the orphanage and were sent to the same school. The three used to jump onto the tram at the exit and sneak aboard without paying. They were caught once and tried by the Court. As punishment they had to promise not to repeat the offense.

Shmuel was caught again, and this time the punishment was Paragraph 900. Soon after coming off probation he was back at the old game. One morning as he and his friends clambered onto the tram, one boy saw Korczak sitting inside and exclaimed, "There's the doctor. Jump off!"

But it was too late. The doctor had seen them. He waved the boys to come sit by him. The group rode in grim silence until the tram reached the school stop at the corner of Chlodna and Zelazna, where there was also a coffee house. Korczak led the boys off the train and invited them to have tea with him.

One of the boys said they would be late to school. Korczak replied that on this day he would give them notes. When the tea came it was very hot and Korczak warned them to drink it slowly. While the boys sipped their tea he left the table and began to pace around them. The tea and cakes were finally finished, and Korczak stopped pacing. Standing in front of the trio he said in a quiet voice, "You boys are brighter than the others, more successful in achieving things. We have tried to educate you about this particular crime with all the methods we have. It looks as though we haven't succeeded.

"It looks as though we can't do anything else other than send you home. And what will happen to you then? What you did now is a small crime. But you are small children. As you grow up, crime grows with you. Next you will probably steal fruit from the market, then bigger things, and finally be caught and be sent to jail. There you will get the best education to become a professional thief.

"And you, Shmuel, are in the biggest danger of all. Your mother has three children and no time for your education. You got your biggest blow from destiny when your father died. Now you get the second biggest blow."

The doctor stopped his pacing and looked directly at the children. "I am now going to shake your hands," he said, "and you are going to promise me that from now on you will be good boys."

The boys burst into tears, shook the doctor's hand, and promised to be honest in the future.

Shmuel was to learn another lesson from the doctor—one that illustrates Korczak's patient method of educating both children and adults.

When Shmuel entered the orphanage he left a pet bird at home. One day he told Korczak how much he missed the bird and asked for permission to bring it to the orphanage. The following Saturday while Shmuel was returning to Krochmalna 92 on the tram a policeman in the car told him it was against the law to keep a wild bird in a cage. "I am going to release it," he said.

When they reached Shmuel's stop the policeman got off the tram with him, seized the bird cage, and opened the door. The bird flew away. The policeman gave the cage back to Shmuel who was crying bitterly. "If you don't be quiet and go home I will take you to the police station," the officer threatened.

"I don't care," said Shmuel. "Without the bird I won't go home."

A passerby recognized him as one of the children from Krochmalna 92. The policeman grasped Shmuel's hand and led him to the orphanage. The boy's loud wailing attracted the attention of Korczak who shouted from a window that he would be right down.

Korczak asked the policeman what was the matter. The policeman said, "According to the law . . ."

The doctor, who had seen the empty cage and sized up the situation, interrupted, "According to what kind of law? Don't you know that children have their own law. What's forbidden for adults is allowed children under certain conditions. Maybe we were going to release the bird here. You had no right to release it. If we did it the boy would have understood. But the way you did it, you destroyed all our work with him."

The policeman withered under the doctor's attack. Finally, with much embarrassment he said he would be back in half an hour. When he returned he was carrying a basket with a wild bird in it. Korczak put the bird back in the cage and placed it in his office where Shmuel was allowed to see and feed it.

Every time Shmuel came to see the bird, however, the doctor talked with him about birds, cages, and freedom. One day he asked Shmuel what was the dearest thing to the bird. "Food?"

"No. Freedom."

Then he asked Shmuel to learn a sentence in Latin: *Nominem captivabimus nisi jure victum.*

Shmuel asked what the sentence meant.

"Say it twenty-five times without mistakes and I will tell you," promised the doctor.

When Shmuel had learned the sentence Korczak explained that it was the heart of Polish law: "We will imprison the man only after he is taken by law."

Korczak talked with Shmuel so much about freedom and the law that the boy, aware the object of all the discussion was the wild bird in the cage, protested defensively, "You told me you had a bird in a cage once yourself."

"True," said Korczak, "but my bird was a canary, a tame bird who could live only in a cage. If he had been free he would have been unable to find food for himself. He would die."

Shmuel, who could see that his bird was always trying to get out of the cage, finally said, "I think perhaps we should let my bird go."

The boy and the doctor went out into the orphanage courtyard. Shmuel opened the cage, and the bird flew away. Korczak smiled, and so did Shmuel.

6

ALBERT BREYER HAUS WAS A LARGE BUILDING IN PRAGA which had once been the office of a construction firm. From the street the building had a respectable, even friendly appearance, with flower boxes at the windows and walls covered with ivy which was trimmed and nurtured by three Polish gardeners.

Two sentry boxes with a black swastika in a white circle on either side were the only outward sign that the building had been taken over by the military. The Poles, however, avoided the street: too few of them who had entered here had ever been heard from again.

80

A huge green tile stove dominated one end of the second-floor office of SS Sturmbannfuehrer Dr. Ludwig Hahn. The office had belonged to the president of the firm: a Jew who had been moved into the ghetto. Hahn's ornate oak desk, also appropriated from the former tenant, was at the far end of the room, which was lit principally by two large windows. Hahn had had the handsome wallpaper whitewashed, but he had left the heavy green velvet drapes which, with the desk, were the only reflections of the room's former elegance. A framed color portrait of the Fuehrer, smiling and in full uniform, had been hung in place of an original Bonnard, which was now on its way to the NSD Museum in Berlin.

The Bonnard had been carefully hidden in a package of office supplies which the former owner smuggled into the ghetto. When taking over the office, however, General Hahn had noticed that a wall calendar did not quite fill the outline the Bonnard had left on the wallpaper. Diligent questioning of former employees ultimately revealed that there had been a painting which had disappeared the day before the Germans arrived.

Hahn had ordered the two teen-age children of the firm president taken hostage until the missing picture was returned. Afterward he had ordered one of the children shot as an example to other Jews who, despite German orders, might wish to take some of their valuable furnishings with them into the ghetto.

Sitting at his desk, Hahn once again glanced at the markings on his map. Then he folded it, put it into a drawer. Almost immediately there was a knock at his door.

It was 9:00 A.M. Hoeffle, the Delegate in Charge of Re-settlement Matters, had arrived at Hahn's office to make his report on the intial phase of the Extraordinary Pacification Action, the top-secret AB Aktion. Hoeffle was completely bald except for a patch of a dozen or more hairs which grew over his left ear and which he zealously combed so there was a thin stripe of hair over his head. He wore a V on his left sleeve, indicating he had been an early member of Hitler's NSDAP party.

Hoeffle had been friends for years with the slim, polished Protestant doctor of law and SS general. Both men shared a passion for power, for planning, for pulling strings and watching others dance. Although to their colleagues they were close-mouthed and guarded, they disclosed to each other the inner workings of their art, taking a professional delight in constructing the machinery which spun a tightening net around the Jews.

Hahn was disciplined, a methodical man who took pride in never showing a trace of human warmth. He accomplished everything to which he set his hand with thoroughness, industry, and skill, but he took it all as a chess game; there was nothing which went past his nerves and touched his heart. In his eyes the Jews were outside the category of human beings. He believed that Nazi anti-Semitism was the logical culmination of the millennial Christian teaching that the Jew was the killer of God. For the Warsaw ghetto he was the architect of destruction. Hoeffle was the technician.

Not even in private, however, did either man discuss the final fate of the "resettled" Jews. To have done so, even between themselves, would have been a punishableby-death breach of the Fuehrer's order of September 25, 1941, which specified:

1. No one; no office, no official, no employee, and no worker may be informed of a matter which is to be kept secret, if it is not absolutely necessary for him to have cognizance of it for official reasons.

2. No office, no official, no employee, and no worker may have any more information about a matter which is to be kept secret than is absolutely necessary for the execution of his assignment.

3. No office, no official, no employee, and no worker may be informed of that part of the matter to be kept secret, which pertains to him, any sooner than is absolutely necessary for the execution of his assignment.

4. The thoughtless forwarding of decrees, orders, and information, the secrecy of which is of decisive importance, because some general distribution key is in use, is hereby prohibited.

Hoeffle showed Hahn copies of the order which he planned to give to the Jewish Council on the following morning. While the General read, Hoeffle removed his rimless glasses and fingered the thin bridge of his nose where the glasses had pinched a groove. He had the sallow, gray look of a man who worked too much, slept too little, and got along without regular meals and exercise. He was completely undistinguished except for his darting, alert eyes and unexpectedly powerful hands.

"To assure their proper attention," Hoeffle said, "we plan to take hostages this morning at eleven hundred hours."

"And what alternative do you have if they refuse to agree to the order?" Hahn asked.

"They will sign," promised Hoeffle.

"I put the matter in your hands, then." The statement sounded like a threat, which in fact, it was. The general then looked directly into Hoeffle's eyes. "Now that you have satisfied me that the first day's deportation of seven thousand Jews will go as scheduled, I want you to increase the daily rate to ten thousand."

Hoeffle's face froze, and he raised his hands as if to protest. But he saw the cold look in Hahn's eyes and brought his hands back to his lap.

"Don't look so put upon," Hahn said. "I may have some help for you. I am working on a plan to remove the orphans from the ghetto. I think you said there were three thousand of them?"

"Has Korczak agreed to set the example?" Hoeffle asked hopefully.

"Not yet. But I think we may be able to convince him to leave quietly."

7

SS Untersturmfuehrer Erwin Schneider took pleasure in placing his booted right foot on the white sheet of his bed and lightly passing a hand towel marked Hotel Metropole over its already glistening black leather. He would never have done it to an army cot, but this was Warsaw, not the Eastern Front, and he consciously intended to take advantage of his position as a victor in this city and relax his personal discipline until he assumed the duties of his new, and as yet unknown, assignment.

He polished his left boot, threw aside the hand towel,

and started walking toward the other side of the room. One step was all he was able to take before turning back to the bed, brushing his boot marks carefully from the sheet, and throwing the soiled hand towel into the linen hamper in the bathroom. He could not relax his habits.

Erwin stood in front of the bathroom mirror. Despite the combat he had seen, he remained a cheerful-looking boy of twenty-three who wore with pride his black uniform with the row of ribbons and the silver lightning flashes on its collar which identified him as a member of the elite SS.

Whenever Erwin was anxious about something, as he was now, the sight of himself dressed in full military regalia helped reassure him. His uniform and what it represented filled the hollowness carved in him by the deaths of his mother and father. The neatly pressed cloth was all the family he needed: the brotherhood of the German officer corps. He was not an orphan, abandoned and alone. He was a child of the New Order. Its doctrine, the laws by which he governed his life, was the basis of his strength.

The phone rang.

"Untersturmfuehrer Schneider speaking."

"This is the desk, sir. Your car has arrived."

Erwin thanked the orderly and hung up the phone. He went to the window, which was on the fourth floor front of the hotel, and glanced down toward the street. There was an open, green Mercedes parked at the curb. He watched as its driver, a sergeant, lit a cigarette and leaned against its front fender. A pennant fluttering near the hood signified that this was General Hahn's own staff car.

Erwin left his room and took the elevator down to the lobby of the hotel. On the way he tried to convince himself that his mounting anxiety was nothing more than a natural excitement at meeting his superior officer for the first time, but he could not shake the shadow of apprehension that clouded his thoughts. He had fought well on the Eastern Front for the past eleven months, was even up for a citation. Why then, without notice or explanation, had he been relieved from his battlefield duties four days ago and suddenly transferred to the Command of SS Sturmbannfuehrer Hahn?

The elevator creaked to a halt and Erwin stepped out into the lobby, crowded with officers making their way to the dining room for breakfast. The Metropole had a reputation for serving excellent food.

Outside the hotel, a lance corporal standing guard made the mistake of giving him a sloppy salute. Erwin exploded.

"You are wearing a German Army uniform," Erwin snapped. "I want to hear you heels click and see your sleeve whip out when you salute. Again!"

The corporal's heels clicked, his sleeve snapped audibly, but his "Heil Hitler" came out as one mumbled word.

A colonel and his aide stopped on the sidewalk to watch the spectacle. Their amusement annoyed Erwin, and he went on in a voice brittle with anger: "Again! Because you are not at the front is no reason not to act like a soldier!"

The corporal was sweating by this time, but his second salute was impeccable. Erwin returned it and walked stiffly down the steps to the sidewalk. Forewarned, General Hahn's driver saluted with precision, then held the door for him while he climbed into the back seat of the car.

Erwin's black mood was eased somewhat by the time the car had gone a few blocks. He studied the streets of Warsaw, and then the general's driver. Sergeant Obermayer was a model of military deportment. He drove with his hands at the proper ten-to-one position and never took his eyes off the road ahead. A well-trained soldier, Erwin thought, the kind of superior SS trooper he had had under his command at the Eastern Front.

The cobblestoned road from the Metropole to SS headquarters was lined with dusty trees. Foot traffic and vehicles crowded the road. Glum-faced women dressed in ersatz wool trousers, drab blouses, and wooden-soled shoes were walking to market. They carried poultry in wickerwork cages or pushed barrows loaded with produce. Occasionally one gave the staff car a sullen glance, then plodded wearily on.

At one point along the way Sergeant Obermayer had to brake hard to avoid running into a bullock cart that crowded the center of the road. Erwin leaned over the front seat and impatiently honked the car's horn. The cart did not move aside. Just as Erwin stood up to shout at the driver, the man pulled over and allowed the staff car to pass. When they drew abreast of the wagon, Erwin looked directly into the driver's eyes. What he saw disturbed him. The man was smiling crookedly, his eyes mirroring contempt and hate.

Sergeant Obermayer accelerated away from the cart, but the look in the man's eyes troubled Erwin. "Stubborn Poles," he thought. "By now they should have sense enough to accept the New Order. But they still hate us. They haven't changed."

Farther along they passed a park. Children on summer vacation were shouting and running after a soccer ball. Seeing them made Erwin recall his four months in the orphanage on Cedrowa Street. He could hear again the taunting voices of the other children, tormenting him because he was German and could not speak Polish. Even after he had learned to communicate a little in their language they continued to mock his accent.

By the time Sergeant Obermayer pulled to a halt in front of SS headquarters, Erwin was filled with gloomy misgivings. Warsaw held only unpleasant memories for him.

Erwin entered Albert Breyer Haus after being smartly saluted by a guard on duty in one of the sentry boxes. An old Polish gardener nodded servilely as he passed. Inside he was directed to the second floor where he presented his orders to Sergeant Yeager, the general's secretary.

Sergeant Yeager glanced at Erwin's papers. "Please be seated, Lieutenant," he said. "I will tell the general you are here."

Erwin remained standing. The sergeant pulled a manila dossier from his file, then stepped out from behind his desk. He went to the general's door, rapped once, and opened it.

When Erwin was summoned he stepped into the office, saluted briskly, and remained standing at attention. The presence of Hoeffle, sitting silently off to one side of the room, increased his anxiety. The only Germans wearing civilian clothes in combat areas were Gestapo.

"You have an excellent record," Hahn said.

"Thank you, sir," Erwin answered curtly. He was relieved. Nothing was wrong. For the first time he was able to focus on Hahn. He liked what he saw: strength, purpose, a firm, disciplined officer.

"Sit," Hahn told him.

Erwin sat stiffly on the edge of a straight-backed chair facing the general's desk.

"Your arrival today is most fortuitous," Hahn said blandly. "We are this morning taking the first step in the elimination of the ghetto."

The muscles in Erwin's jaw tightened. Hahn tapped a white note pad on his desk.

"Tomorrow seven thousand Jews will be deported to the East. The day after, ten thousand. By the end of the month we will have seen to it that the majority of subhumans in the area will be en route to the East for resettlement."

"There is, however, a minor problem which I believe you can assist us with."

"At your service, sir," Erwin said, and stiffened as though he had saluted.

"There are half a million Jews in the ghetto," Hahn said softly. He leaned forward. "I have less than fifty SS men and some five hundred Ukranians and Letts under my command in the city. If there was a full-scale rebellion, for example, and every Jew required a bullet in the head, I have barely enough ammunition for the job."

Hahn was smiling at Erwin, speaking intimately as if asking for a particular kind of understanding.

"So you realize," he went on, "why I cannot afford any such outbreak."

90

Erwin had no idea where this was leading, but he nodded mechanically.

"There are three thousand orphans in the ghetto," Hahn continued, "all of them no better than parasites who require food and care but contribute nothing to our cause. They must be resettled promptly—and without creating any disturbance."

Hahn turned aside for the moment, then swung back and stared coldly at Erwin. "You are an orphan, aren't you?"

"Yes, sir," Erwin replied. The tone of Hahn's voice and the sudden change in the tenor of the conversation startled and frightened him. Again he became aware of the silent man in civilian clothes. Was he Gestapo? Was there something wrong? Could one of his own ancestors have been a Jew? He was completely unnerved.

"You lived in an orphanage here in Warsaw?" said Hahn.

Erwin nodded mutely. Hoeffle looked up in surprise.

"The orphanage was run by Henryk Goldszmidt?"

Erwin was puzzled. "I don't know a Henryk Goldszmidt," he said.

"Henryk Goldszmidt, alias Janusz Korczak," the *nom de plume* under which Korczak had become famous. His real name was long forgotten by all but old friends.

"I know Dr. Korczak," Erwin said. Vividly, in the space of a moment, he saw himself as a child, wide-eyed and trembling, stripped to the waist and reluctantly standing behind a glowing fluoroscope in the Institute of Specialized Pedagogy in Warsaw.

There were twenty-three medical students in the room

and the doctor was lecturing. On the screen the students could see the image of Erwin's heart beating wildly.

Korczak spoke quietly: "Here, gentlemen! Look at this heart and remember forever what you now see. . . . When children are naughty, when you feel angry, tired, or irritable, and you feel you must punish them, then remember, this is what the heart of a frightened child looks like. I have been through three wars. I have seen terrible sights. But I tell you that the cruelest thing to witness is a terrified child."

Later Erwin learned that the doctor had purposely chosen him as his "associate" for the lecture, knowing such an honor would give him status among the other children.

"Korczak is a symbol to the Jews in the ghetto, and especially to the leaders of the other orphanages," Erwin heard the general saying. Erwin nodded and ran his hands nervously across the knees of his uniform. He sought to calm himself, to find customary reassurance in the uniform.

"If he cooperates," Hahn continued, "and reports voluntarily for resettlement with his children, he will set an example that the others will follow. On the other hand, if we have to use force to evacuate the children, we stand the risk of making a martyr of Korczak. Do you understand, Lieutenant?"

"Yes, sir," Erwin answered.

"Martyrs are dangerous," Hahn went on. "Korczak has all the marking of one. The American press interviewed him just after the occupation, and he used the opportunity to cause Berlin a great deal of embarrassment."

Hahn leaned back in his chair and removed the swagger stick from its place inside his boot. Holding the stick in his right hand, he began gently tapping his left palm. "So," he said, "now you know why I had you transferred to my command. You happened to have known this Jew through no fault of your own, and I am sure you can talk sense to him."

Hahn held the swagger stick to his right eye, squinted at Erwin as if he were a painter measuring him with a brush, and added, "Your assignment is to get Goldszmidt and his orphans to report voluntarily to the Umschlagplatz within five days. How you do it is your affair."

Hahn then pushed Erwin's dossier to one side, signaling the end of the interview. Erwin remained rooted to his chair.

"Have you any questions, Lieutenant?" Hahn asked.

"Just one, sir," Erwin said.

"What is it?" Hahn asked impatiently.

Erwin glanced at the man in civilian clothes, then said, "I have heard at the front that the Jews are not being resettled. There are rumors that they are being exterminated."

"Do not discuss rumors with me," Hahn said quietly. Although he had not raised his voice, he radiated an icy anger.

"Well, sir . . . I meant," Erwin fumbled. "What if Korczak has heard the rumors and refuses to leave the ghetto?"

Hahn took his swagger stick and thoughtfully tapped the desk. From the large clean-shaven face his clear gray eyes looked into Erwin's.

"The rumors are false," he said. "They were started by the Jews themselves to get sympathy from the world press and their racial brothers in America. But even if the rumors were true—which I assure you they are not—I do not need to remind you of Point Four of the Duties of the German soldier: 'Obedience is the foundation of the Wehrmacht, trust is the foundation of obedience.' Your orders are to get them to go!"

"Yes, sir," said Erwin.

At that moment, Sergeant Yeager knocked and entered the office. Hahn glanced up.

"The merchant is here, sir," Yeager said. "He gave me this to show you."

The sergeant handed Hahn a thin, leather-covered box and left the office. Hahn opened the box and removed a dazzling, diamond-studded necklace. He smiled with approval as it glistened in the sunlight. Then, still holding the necklace, he turned back to Erwin.

"Let me impress upon you that you have this man's life in your hands," Hahn said. "It is only rarely in life that we get a chance to play God. This is your chance."

"Sir?" Erwin said, puzzled.

Hahn stood up. He still held the necklace. When he spoke, his voice was soft and paternal. "You can give Korczak your word as a German officer and gentleman that if he voluntarily reports for resettlement with his children he will not be harmed."

"Yes, sir," Erwin said. Hahn's words were reassuring.

"And you can also promise him a kilo of bread and some marmalade for each child on the day they report voluntarily to the Umschlagplatz. But get this quite straight, Lieutenant," he added quietly. "I expect Korczak and his children at the Umschlagplatz Saturday morning, August 5. Heil Hitler."

The interview was concluded.

8

THE GERMAN HIGH COMMAND HAD PREPARED THE EX-
termination program for the Warsaw ghetto thoughtfully
and carefully. Aktion Reinhardt, its code name, was
subtly conceived, and the Germans by now had had much
practical experience: the ghettos in Lublin, Lodsz, Radom,
had already been emptied of their Jews.

The Nazis were well aware of the danger of letting the
Jews realize they were doomed en masse. An early realiza-
tion of their hopelessness might well have aroused large-
scale resistance, which, even if unarmed, would through

sheer weight of numbers have immensely complicated the extermination enterprise. Therefore two objectives had to be obtained: the Jews had to be separated into conveniently manageable groups; and the knowledge that they were to be murdered had to be kept from them until the last possible moment.

The establishment of ghettos achieved the first purpose. In them the Jews of each city were segregated into groups which could establish no contact with each other or with the outside world. Few people outside of Poland were more than casually aware of the plight of the Jews in the ghettos, and politics, historical prejudice, and callousness silenced any troublesome protests. The Nazis were counting on this indifference, and on the fact that those who knew the truth would not be believed. The Jews themselves expected to be hounded, to be tortured, to be decimated, but the reality of the extermination centers was something they could not believe. Those few reports that did reach them were received with incredulity by the Jewish communities and their leaders.

An integral part of the Aktion was the confiscation of all real property and movables. The Jews were required to leave their apartments outside of the ghetto intact; they were allowed to take only clothing and personal valuables with them, an ironic generosity since ultimately the Germans would get everything. All industrial plants and all the physical assets of business in the East which were owned by the Jews were deeded over to German authorities with only token payments. After being herded into the ghetto, the Jews were furnished with special identity cards and insignia to be sewn on their clothes so that they

97

were easy to recognize. They were then left alone under regulations that made life all but impossible, until the SS could organize the utilization of the confiscated business properties and prepare the next resting place for the Jews.

The first phase of the Warsaw Aktion took place in September 1940, when the Warsaw ghetto was formed. The second phase—the start of the "resettlement" of the Jews to extermination camps—took place on Tuesday, July 21, 1942, Korczak's sixty-third birthday. At 11:00 A.M. four Sicherheitsdienst cars and a truck drove up in front of the main building of the Jewish Council at Grzybowska 26–28. Eighteen SD and SS personnel marched into the building. Three of the SS officers with revolvers drawn stormed into Chairman Adam Czerniakow's office and commanded him to call a meeting of the Judenrat at once.

Only eleven of the twenty-four members of the council were in the building. Without explanation or waiting for the other councilors to arrive, the Germans herded them into the truck and told Czerniakow to remain in his office.

During the afternoon, while the seized members of the Judenrat sat behind bars in Pawiak Prison, flying squads of German police ranged through the ghetto. They singled out relatively well-dressed Jews and, without discussion or even troubling to ask for identity cards, shot them on the spot.

Between seventy-five and one hundred upper-class Jews were killed in this way. One other man was murdered— Professor Dr. Raszeja, a non-Jew who was visiting the ghetto in the course of his medical duties. He was in possession of an official pass, but the Nazis were not interested in technicalities that day.

Early in the morning of Wednesday, July 22, a cordon of Junaks, Ukranians, Lithuanians, Latvians, and Germans tightly sealed off the entire ghetto. Soldiers armed with machine pistols were posted every thirty paces around the entire ghetto wall.

At 9:00 A.M. two trucks containing Ukranian militiamen pulled up in front of the Judenrat and surrounded the building. A dozen SS men marched into Chairman Adam Czerniakow's office on the first floor.

"What is it?" Czerniakow asked. "What do you want?"

He was given no answer until Hoeffle, the Delegate for Resettlement Affairs, briskly walked in, a leather briefcase in his hand.

"You will call a meeting of your council immediately," Hoeffle snapped.

Czerniakow nodded toward his secretary. "Quickly," he said.

The chairman's secretary ran from office to office summoning the remaining members of the council. In a trembling voice she impressed on everyone the urgent need for haste. Meanwhile, Jewish policemen were hastily arranging chairs in the conference room while SS enlisted men were herding all Judenrat employees who would not be attending the meeting into an upstairs room at the rear of the building.

When the council was assembled, the members were instructed to sit together along one side of the conference table. An equal number of Germans sat opposite them. The Germans stared coldly across the table. The Jews fearfully avoided their gaze.

There was deathly silence when Hoeffle strutted to the head of the conference table. He did not sit down.

"Pay particular attention to what you are about to hear," Hoeffle began. He dug some papers from his briefcase. "I am about to dictate to you an order for the removal of the entire Jewish population of the Warsaw ghetto."

A horrified, quiet moan filled the room.

"Quiet," Hoeffle demanded, throwing his briefcase on the table with a bang. The members of the council froze. "You had better hear me well . . . every word!"

Czerniakow glanced at his secretary. She sat ready to take down Hoeffle's order.

"I am entrusting part of the responsibility for the execution of this order to the Judenrat," Hoeffle barked. "If the Judenrat proves incapable, all—I repeat—*all* of its members will be executed!"

Hoeffle then turned to his notes—the Germans never gave the Jews written orders. Outside the window, a German scout car driver, the curved magazine of a model 58 assault gun cradled in his arms, had his radio turned up to full volume. He was listening to a Polish dance band playing "The Lambeth Walk."

"All right, we start," Hoeffle said. Quietly and in a monotonous voice, he read the endless document in heavily accented Polish. The chamber was hot, flies buzzed, and from the crowd of men in heavy clothes arose an exhalation of rank sweat and the smell of fear itself.

The few strands of hair Hoeffle combed from behind his ear and over his bald head had been jostled out of place. He was conscious of this and tried unsuccessfully to rearrange them all the while he spoke.

Article Number One: All Jewish inhabitants of Warsaw, irrespective of sex or age, will be resettled in the East.

Article Number Two: The following categories are exempt from resettlement:

A. All Jews employed by German authorities or enterprises who are able to submit proof of it.

B. All Jews who are members or employees of the Jewish Council as of the day of publishing of this order.

Hoeffle looked up from his papers. An audible sigh of relief came from the Jewish side of the conference table. Hoeffle smiled crookedly. Then he went on with his reading, his voice mechanical and dull.

C. All Jews employed by firms belonging to the German Reich, who are able to submit proof of it.

D. All Jews fit for work but not yet covered by the employment procedure; these are to be isolated in the Jewish quarter.

E. All Jews enrolled in the Jewish Guard.

At that, a stocky, young member of the Jewish Guard who was barring the doorway gave a choking cough from nervous relief. Hoeffle looked at him and shouted, "Get out in the hall if you can't keep quiet!"

The guard swallowed his cough, and Hoeffle continued.

F. All Jews belonging to the personnel of Jewish hospitals as well as those enrolled in Jewish Sanitary Columns.

Hoeffle again looked at the members of the council and laughing caustically said, "Most likely you'll be swamped by people carrying 'dreck' buckets and brooms." Then the smile turned into a scowl as he added, "But, remember! These orders are effective as of now. Last-minute enrollment in any of these categories will not be tolerated!"

He waited for a comment from the council. There was none. The members maintained a frozen silence. Their ashen faces and the beads of perspiration on their foreheads betrayed their thoughts and feelings. Hoeffle allowed himself to enjoy their agony for a moment, then went back to his reading.

G. All Jews, members of immediate families of persons enumerated under categories A to F only; only wives and children are considered members of families.

Hoeffle leaned forward and, clarifying his last statement, hissed, "That means no mothers, no fathers, no aunts, uncles, cousins or the like . . . just wives and children!"

Again there was no comment from the council.

"Good," Hoeffle smirked. "We understand each other . . ." He went back to his notes.

H. All Jews who on the first day of resettlement find themselves in one of the Jewish hospitals and are not fit to be released. The unfitness for release must be dated by a physician designated by the Jewish Council.

"This last sentence in Section H," he added, again looking down the row of councilors, "was a necessary point to include, don't you think?" It was a question for which he expected no answer. "I mean," he smiled crookedly, "you could imagine the rush you would have had into your already overcrowded hospitals."

The Germans sitting at the conference table laughed heartedly. Hoeffle waited for quiet before continuing.

Article Number Three: Every Jewish deportee is per-

mitted to take 15 kilograms of his property as traveling luggage. Luggage above that weight will be confiscated. All precious objects such as money, jewels, gold, etc., may be taken along.

Article Number Four: Resettlement begins July 22, 1942, 11:00 P.M.

It was at this point that the members of the council suddenly reacted. Hoeffle's naming of the date—that very night—drove home the reality of the situation to them, and they broke into a whispered discussion, strained and intense.

"Quiet!" shouted Hoeffle. "Save your chattering for later. I'm not finished yet."

"But Herr Hoeffle . . ." Czerniakow started.

"No questions!" said Hoeffle, cutting him off. "I am not here to debate any of these points with you. These orders," he slapped the pages he held, "are meant to be obeyed, totally, immediately, and without question. Save your haggling until I am finished. I do not want to listen to it."

Hoeffle gesticulated so wildly that the few hairs he had labored to get into place again shook loose. This angered him, and he thumped his fist on the table shouting, "You will be shot if you do not comply! I have the authority!"

The Jews looked across the table at the uniformed Germans opposite them, then fell into an uneasy silence. Hoeffle turned his back on the council, quickly smoothed down his hair, then returned to the reading of his proclamation.

"The following instructions for the duration of resettlement are given to the Jewish Council. For their carrying out"—he swept the conference table with a hostile glare—"the members of the Jewish Council are responsible with their lives."

Article Number One: The Jewish Council receives orders concerning resettlement from the Delegate for Resettlement Affairs or his deputy only. For the duration of the resettlement, the Jewish Council will elect a special committee for resettlement matters, whose chairman is the President of the Jewish Council, and deputy chairman, the Commandant of the Jewish Guard.

Article Number Two: The Jewish Council is responsible for producing the Jews designated for daily resettlement. In order to accomplish that task, the Jewish Council is to use the Jewish Guard. The Jewish Council is to see to it that six thousand Jews are delivered daily, not later than 4:00 P.M., to the assembly place beginning July 22, 1942.

Czerniakow began to raise another question, but was prudently silenced by the council member sitting next to him.

The assembly place for the duration of the evacuation is the Jewish Hospital at Stawki Street. On July 22, 1942, six thousand Jews are to be delivered directly to the loading station at the Transferstelle. For the time being the Jewish Council may draw the daily quota of Jews from the general population. Later on, the Jewish Council will receive definite instructions as to the parts of streets or housing blocks to be emptied.

At that point the radio in the German scout car ceased broadcasting music and started in on a news report. Competition with another voice annoyed Hoeffle, and he indicated that he wanted the radio turned off. One of the Germans sitting at the conference table stood, walked to the window, and shouted at the driver outside. There was an immediate silence, and the German returned to his seat at the table. Hoeffle started reading again.

Article Number Three: On July 23, 1942, the Jewish Council is to evacuate the Jewish Hospital at Stawki Street and to transfer the patients and staff to another suitable building inside the ghetto so that on the evening of July 23, 1942, the hospital may be ready to receive daily the Jews to be resettled.

Article Number Four: Furthermore, the Jewish Council has to see to it that objects and property left by these Jews, unless infected, are taken and registered in special assembly points to be designated. For that purpose the Jewish Council should use the Jewish Guard and a proper number of Jewish laborers. This activity will be supervised by the Sicherheitspolizei which will issue special instructions to the Jewish Council. Illegal appropriation of these objects and property will be punished by death.

Hoeffle, apparently wanting to hurry to the conclusion of his declaration, read faster. Czerniakow's secretary, her hair falling over her forehead, had difficulty keeping up with him. The other members of the Council, including Czerniakow himself, sat motionless in their chairs, faces blank with shock.

Article Number Five: The Jewish Council also must see to it that Jews employed in German enterprises or by German authorities continue their work during the action. To carry out this order, the Jewish Council will issue proper announcements to the Jewish population sup-

ported by heaviest penalties. The Jewish Council will also see to it that there is no pause in the functioning of such Jewish supply enterprises as will be required to secure the feeding of the Jews gathered at the assembly point as well as of the remaining Jews.

Article Number Six: The Jewish Council is responsible for burying, on the day of death, Jews deceased during the resettlement period.

Article Number Seven: The Jewish Council will post the following announcements to the Jewish population of Warsaw: "On the order of the German authorities all Jewish inhabitants of Warsaw will be resettled in the East . . . etc."

Hoeffle's throat went dry momentarily. He cleared it and said, "That is, from points one to four. Understood?" He glanced at the members of the council. Automatically, most of them nodded affirmatively.

"Good," he said. "Now we get to the penalties." He paused to let the words sink in.

Article Number Eight: Section A. Every Jew who does not belong nor has so far the right to belong to Group 2, Points A and C, and who leaves the Jewish quarter after the start of resettlement, will be shot.

Section B. Every Jew who undertakes a move which may circumvent or disturb the carrying out of the resettlement orders will be shot.

C. Every Jew who assists a move which may circumvent or disturb the carrying out of the resettlement orders will be shot.

D. All Jews not belonging to categories enumerated under Point 2, A to H, who are found in Warsaw after the conclusion of the resettlement will be shot.

106

At that moment, a short burst of machine-gun fire was heard. It came from the direction of the far wall of the ghetto at Dzika Street and was quite muffled. But its effect was pronounced. Every member of the council stiffened as though he himself had been hit by the bullets.

Hoeffle smiled. To have his words punctuated so dramatically obviously pleased him. He seemed to relish the moment briefly before concluding the meeting with: "The Jewish Council is warned that should its instructions and orders not be carried out, a proper number of hostages will be taken and shot. Warsaw, July 22, 1942. Dictated by the Delegate for Deportation Matters."

Hoeffle carefully replaced his notes in his briefcase and, saying "That is all," turned on his heels and left the building. He was followed by the Germans and the Jewish guards.

At first the Jews in the conference room sat stunned. Then, after the German trucks and cars started up and pulled away, bedlam broke out. Everyone talked at once; remonstrating, arguing, wailing, and trying to determine his own circumstances relative to the proclamation.

The confusion heightened when those employees of the Judenrat who had been locked in the upstairs room came bursting into the conference room to learn what had happened.

In the midst of this tumult, Czerniakow, pale as death, shaking, silently left the room. Two councilmen hastened his secretary off to type up the orders so that posters might be prepared.

Forty minutes later, with the sounds of confusion and hysteria still pouring out of the conference room, Czerniakow's secretary entered the chairman's office.

"I prepared them as fast as I could," she said and placed the original sheets of the typewritten orders on Czerniakow's desk. "With your approval, I'll have a copy sent to the printer right away."

The secretary stood at the desk while Czerniakow, still pale but no longer trembling, read the orders. When he came to the last page, he looked up at his secretary. "There is an error here," he said in a husky voice.

"Where?" the secretary asked. She leaned over and read aloud the line his finger pointed to. *Adam Czerniakow, Chief Engineer, Chairman of the Judenrat.* The secretary was puzzled. In the past, all the instructions to the ghetto populace had been signed in exactly that way.

"There is nothing wrong with that, Mr. Czerniakow," the secretary said.

"Yes there is," Czerniakow said. He picked up a pen and crossed out his name. "This is one proclamation that will not receive my endorsement."

The secretary gasped. It was as if she had just watched him sign his own death warrant.

Czerniakow pushed the papers back to her. "Now I know why they arrested them," he said bitterly, referring to the eleven members of the Judenrat that the Germans had seized the day before and then released. "It was so they could sign this document."

The secretary pleaded with Czerniakow to allow his name to remain on the proclamation. He ignored her. Clenching his fists, he stared vacantly at the wall while tears flowed down his cheeks.

9

Erwin Schneider was temporarily assigned to a militia formation of twenty-five men under the command of SS Obersturmfuehrer Klostermayer. He reported for his first day's duty at a street corner and awaited his orders. When the entire company had assembled, he learned that only seven of them were Germans. The rest were Junaks— Ukranians and Lithuanians. His commander, arriving in the lead car of a small column of cars and trucks, leaped to the sidewalk and immediately started barking orders. While the formation climbed into the vehicles, Erwin introduced himself to the captain.

"We need all the help we can get, Oberleutnant," Klostermayer said. "The quotas aren't easy to manage."

Klostermayer, knowing that Erwin had come from the front, then added in a confidential tone, "You'll find this a different kettle of fish than you're used to. Hang back if you like until you get a stomach for it. Take your lead from the sergeant. Tomorrow, however, I will expect you to carry your own weight. Tonight, if things go well, I'll let you buy me a drink."

Erwin accepted Klostermayer's suggestion and did not become too embroiled in the action which followed. This enabled him to observe more clearly, act by act, the day's operations.

During the first stage of the work, Erwin noted that there was a well-planned military technique in the way his unit approached the action. They singled out a house and blockaded it. Once the entrances and exits were closed off, the German enlisted men and Junaks, armed with machine pistols, rifles, and revolvers, stormed the staircases shouting at the tops of their voices, "All Jews out . . . all Jews downstairs." From that moment on, any similarity to a military operation ceased.

Jews, old, young, infirm, were shoved and beaten down the stairways and onto the streets. Those found trying to hide inside the buildings, as well as those who were too sick to move, were instantly shot and killed.

Once the Jews were out in the street, Klostermayer took over and carefully scrutinized all their documents. Jews not holding that day's valid work card were stuffed into cars and trucks and transported to the Umschlagplatz, assembly point for "deportees."

At one point there were not enough cars and trucks to handle the load. Erwin's group was given an old farm wagon.

"Where are the horses?" Erwin asked the sergeant.

"Wait a minute," the sergeant said and smiled. "You'll see."

At that, several husky young Jews and a few old men were shoved out of a building and forced between the shafts. They were the animals who were whipped into pulling the overloaded cart full of wailing Jews to the Umschlagplatz.

Erwin, along with several Junaks and three German soldiers, provided the armed escort for the wagon as it was hauled slowly through the streets. Above the wretched grunting of the Jews straining between the shafts and the crying of those heaped into the wagon, Erwin heard the hysterical screaming of a dark, full-breasted young woman running and stumbling barefooted after them. She was trying to get back her child, who had been snatched from her arms in front of her building and who was now lying crushed and weeping beneath the tangle of knees, feet, and buttocks on the wagon floor. The sound of the woman's high-pitched voice was nerve-shattering. A German soldier walking alongside Erwin turned and with the air of one whose patience has been overtaxed kicked her squarely in the groin and without a second look returned to the side of the wagon.

The scene that greeted Erwin at the Umschlagplatz might well have been pictured in Dante's Inferno. He did not know which shocked him more: the sight of the human cargo spilling out of the trucks, beaten into a tight,

111

writing mass by the soldiers, or the sound of terror rising from the square, a horrifying, pulsing note made up of the groans, screams, and sobs of thousands of tortured souls.

There were two squares at the Umschlagplatz. The first was where the "selection" took place. Here the masses were funneled through a narrow entrance at which, on either side, stood pairs of SS men. For a moment they could be seen as individuals: mothers with babies in their arms, well-dressed, upper-class men, peasants clinging to lumpy bundles, pretty girls, tottering old folk.

Male Jews who were declared fit for physical labor were directed to the "Dulag" from which they would later be sent to various labor camps. Occasionally the selection was held up momentarily while a shop manager loudly intervened to save a skilled worker, and those few fortunate men were shoved out to freedom. The overwhelming majority were herded to the nearby train tracks. There they were packed by blows and pushing into cattle cars, until they were a solid mass of wailing, bleeding humanity.

After the day's work was completed and the Umschlagplatz cleared, Erwin reported to Klostermayer.

"You are relieved, Lieutenant," the obersturmfuehrer told him. "You will be notified where to report tomorrow. Now," he said, his official duties complied with, "the day did go well. How about that drink?"

"Yes, sir," Erwin said. "It would be my pleasure."

Klostermayer drove Erwin to a small café in Praga. Erwin bought the first round of drinks. "After this," the captain said, "the rest of the evening is on me. Call it a treat to a deflowered virgin."

Erwin felt his cheeks flush. Klostermayer laughed, ordered food and drinks for them, then asked him a peculiar question.

"Would you like to go upstairs with me before dinner?"

"Upstairs, sir?"

"They keep some tarts up there. If you'd like, I'll let you take the redhead . . . but only for tonight."

"No thank you, sir. I appreciate your offer. But the day . . ."

"Yes, I know," Klostermayer interjected. "The day has been too trying."

Klostermayer pushed his chair back and stood up. "You'll learn," he said. "You're new yet. Give you a few days at it and you'll discover your own formula to get it to roll off your back." He turned and disappeared up a flight of stairs at the rear of the café.

Erwin drank an entire bottle of wine in the fifteen minutes it took for the captain to return to the table.

"Ah," Klostermayer said. "My timing is infallible."

Erwin glanced up. The waiter was bringing their meal.

Although Klostermayer devoured his food with gusto, Erwin hardly touched his. He had, however, consumed another bottle of wine and a large glass of plum brandy by the time the meal was over. He was more than a little drunk when the captain asked him ("in confidence, mind you") for his impressions of the operation.

Erwin slowly considered the question in his fogged mind. As a front-line soldier he was appalled at what he had seen on the streets of Warsaw that day. The expulsion action was equivalent in military terms to mopping up a piece of terrain, but with one significant difference: at the front, those of the enemy who are still alive after the action surrender, and are not beaten or shot after they do.

The Jews of Warsaw were not military antagonists to Erwin. They were the least warlike of civilians. Although he did not doubt that Germany and the conquered territories had to be purged of Jews for military reasons, he saw no reason for brutality.

He thought, too, of the Junaks shooting unarmed Jews and mused cynically that it had always been that way, that foreigners had always been crueler than Germans. As for the Germans who shot civilians, he rationalized that they were rear-line troops and that, in his experience, the second wave of troops was always worse to the occupied peoples than the fighting forces.

As an officer, what distressed him most about the day was the number of SS troops and experienced soldiers he had seen on duty. Why was so much effective manpower being squandered in Warsaw instead of being utilized at the front? The Hitler Youth, it seemed to him, would have been just as capable of handling the Jewish deportations to the East.

"Lieutenant," he heard the captain say, "I did not expect you to fall into such a trance when I asked you about the day."

"I'm sorry, sir," Erwin said. "I was just thinking that it was a messy job at best, but one that has to be done."

10

THE FIRST DAY'S RESETTLEMENT QUOTA HAD BEEN EASILY
attained. The Jewish police had rounded up 6,289 Jews.
Most were scooped out of the notorious "Death Points."
These were charity refuges for homeless people into
which the poverty-stricken Jews from the provinces had
poured. The refuges acquired their somber name during
the typhus epidemic of a year earlier. There was a method
in choosing the inhabitants of the "Death Points" as a
beginning toward filling the quota: most of these people
were three-quarters dead anyway. Next the Jewish police

emptied the jails, particularly the Gensia Street Prison where those convicted of petty infractions of rules had been confined. Finally, the police drove beggars in off the streets and finished the day by taking a number of incurable cases from the hospital.

Friday's roundup, however, was not progressing satisfactorily when, late in the afternoon, Adam Czerniakow made his final gesture as president of the Judenrat. Although he had been one of those members of the council who had clung desperately to the official story that the deportation would end with the removal of sixty thousand "non-productive" ghetto Jews to places where their work would be useful to the Germans, he was plagued with fears to the contrary, some of which he had revealed in confidence to his secretary that morning.

A few minutes before 4:00 P.M. Untersturmfuehrer Hoeffle, accompanied by Wortorf, an assistant in charge of deportations, walked into Czerniakow's office. Czerniakow was seated behind his glass-topped desk, dictating a letter to his secretary. Wortorf, speaking in Polish, told the secretary to leave them. She nodded humbly and went into her own office, which was directly outside Chairman Czerniakow's.

Five minutes later the secretary saw Hoeffle and Wortorf leave the building, and overheard Hoeffle saying, "He asks too many questions for his own health. . . ."

She returned to Czerniakow's office and knocked on his door; now he could complete the letter he had been dictating. When there was no answer she knocked again and walked in. She saw the chairman at his desk, resting his head on his arms. Although she knew he had come to

116

work exhausted that morning, she had never before seen him fall asleep during the day.

She was about to touch his shoulder before she realized that he was dead. At his elbow there was a half-filled glass of water and a small, empty vial of potassium nitrate.

A framed picture of his wife and son lay across his extended left hand. There were two envelopes propped against an inkwell. One was addressed to his son, the other to his wife. In his farewell letter to his wife he asked her to forgive him for abandoning her and to understand that for him to have acted in any other way was impossible.

His daily diary lay open on the desk. The last notations read:

> July 23, 1942—early morning. The community offices. Wortorf of the deportation group came to discuss some matters with me. Exempted the people in the trade schools as well as the men and women in the workshops. About the orphans he advised me to talk things over with Hoeffle.
>
> About the craftsmen he asked me to do the same. To my question about how many days the deportation actions would go on he answered, "Seven days a week." In the city there is a feverish movement to create workshops. A sewing machine can save a life.
>
> 3 P.M. At the moment there are only 1,000 for deportation. According to the order, another 4,000 must be delivered by 4 P.M. . . .

The Germans refused to allow Czerniakow's body to be removed for burial until a new deputy was chosen to replace him. The chairman's body had been laid out on a couch in his office where his wife and two relatives mourned over it. In the council room the members of the Judenrat were closeted trying to select a new chairman, while SS men patrolled the corridors and guarded the office door. No one was allowed to leave the building.

All night long the members of the Judenrat debated. No one wanted the job, and each man nominated firmly resisted the pressure to accept. Finally, in desperation, the members asked Wortorf to make the decision. He appointed Lichtenbaum, an engineer. Over Lichtenbaum's signature a proclamation was posted asking people to report voluntarily for resettlement with their families, so that no household need be split up. As an added inducement each "voluntary" family would receive three kilograms of bread and one kilogram of marmalade per person. (These were to be provided by the Judenrat at its own expense.)

In the early hours of Saturday morning Wortorf allowed the Judenrat to go home and gave permission for the undertaker Pinkert to send two men into the building with a pine coffin. And he gave special permission for a burial service to be conducted the next morning at the Jewish cemetery in Gensia Street, with the express condition that it be held in absolute secrecy with no more than six people present.

The wooden coffin, perched precariously on a two-wheeled cart, was pushed by a pair of husky men from Pinkert's funeral parlor. It was followed by the black-clad, weeping widow, Frau Dr. Felicia Czerniakow, riding in a bicycle-rickshaw. The rabbi, three members of the Jewish council, Korczak, and a few other mourners pedaled behind on bicycles rented from the funeral parlor which specialized in bicycle funerals. ("Aesthetic and practical in all respects," their advertisements claimed.)

Ukranian guards halted the dreary procession at the cemetery's tall iron gates. Six mourners were allowed to buy a cemetery pass for two and a half zlotys. The rest were sent home. Before allowing the cart to enter the walled enclosure, the guards opened the wooden casket and prodded the body for any items which might be hidden there. Coffins had often been used to conceal a family's gold or jewelry in the hopes of retrieving it in a better time.

The mourners traced their way slowly alongside the raised portion of the fifteen-acre cemetery which had been the final resting place of Warsaw Jewry for nine hundred years. They walked up a pathway flanked on the right by a grove of trees. It was a sunny day but the path was in deep shadow. Underfoot last year's unraked leaves covered the path with a spongy carpet. Many headstones had been hauled out and used by the Germans for road construction, and others were lying in disorderly piles.

Ghetto Jews were not normally allowed to bury their dead. Most bodies were hauled to the cemetery in the dark and handed over to the guards. Families had no idea of where or how their relatives were buried, and it was just as well. The Germans had merely dumped the bodies on top of each other in common graves.

"I watched Adam Thursday night," the widow whispered to Korczak. "The way he came home and paced up and down and wouldn't talk about his day the way he always did, but only said, 'They have signed the death

119

sentence of the Jewish people,' and when I asked him what he meant he just stared at me blindly."

The widow's words turned into sobs. Korczak, his arm around her, tried to comfort her. It was difficult walking like this and keeping up with the procession, but he wanted her to feel him strongly at her side. Behind her dark veil, he could see her eyes, red-rimmed with hours of weeping and now overflowing again with tears. He wanted to say something to her, the proper things that people say at such moments, but he could not get out a word. Czerniakow was, after all, a suicide, a man who had violated God's trust according to any religion. It was only because of the terrible times that the rabbi had agreed to allow him to be buried in this sanctified ground.

"Something had happened to him," the widow continued. Her sobs had quieted, but the tears continued flowing freely down her face. "Whatever it was, it drained his strength, destroyed his purpose. His eyes—I knew by his eyes he was thinking of sacrifice. I could feel what he was thinking before he went to the office yesterday, and I was afraid."

Suddenly Frau Czerniakow asked Korczak a direct question. "Do you know why he did this?"

Korczak remained silent.

"I know why he did this," the widow went on. "I know why he did this to himself, to me, to all of us. I've asked myself this question a thousand times since yesterday. He did it because he believed that his sacrifice would awaken the world from its indifference. He did it because he thought, in some way, that his sacrifice would save us all. It was not a selfish thing, an escape. It was a lofty sacrifice.

He wanted to save us all," she cried in rising anguish. "You understand, don't you? You can see that he did it as a sacrifice?"

Korczak could not bring himself to look directly into her eyes, yet he could feel them urging, beseeching him to agree, to sympathize, to say that he believed Adam Czerniakow's abandonment of his wife and his people was a gesture of noble sacrifice. Korczak was torn. Should he say something he did not feel simply to accommodate the desperate woman clinging pitifully to him? Should he help her build an acceptable memory of her dead husband, one that would give her comfort and allow her to face the dreadful days ahead?

While he hesitated he realized the rabbi was looking at him expectantly. Korczak stepped to the foot of the grave. He had been asked to deliver the eulogy, and now every head turned toward him. The Ukranian guards were shifting impatiently.

His voice firm and solemn, Korczak said, "The Lord entrusted you with the honorable task of watching over the dignity of the Jewish people. Now you are honored to bring it back to the Lord."

Korczak returned to the side of Frau Czerniakow.

The rabbi advanced to the corpse and intoned the benediction: *Praised be Thou, Jehovah God, righteous Judge.* With his thick fingers he carefully touched the dead man's eyelids. As the rabbi recited the service, the mourners answered in chorus, *Vain and deceitful and fleeting as wind is the world, but One and Eternal is the God of Israel, the Everlasting, the Infinite, Jehovah.* They plucked grass and cast it behind them, saying, *We are like*

121

the grass that withers. And they said: *We remember that we are dust.*

After the coffin was lowered into the narrow pit and hastily covered with earth, Kaddish was recited. Kaddish, the Prayer for the Dead, is usually spoken by the oldest male member of the family. Czerniakow's son was not present. He was in Russia, fighting with the Red Army; and as the rabbi, in his stead, chanted the ancient Hebrew words, Korczak could not help thinking, hoping, that perhaps one day young Czerniakow would sweep back into Warsaw at the head of an army of steel and take vengeance on the Germans for the death of his father.

Then, the funeral over, the Ukranian guards wasted no time herding the mourners up the path and out of the cemetery.

Except for Czerniakow's widow, no one would have lingered anyway. They were all full of their own problems, all anxious to hurry back to the city to discover what had happened during their absence, to learn what the present day would have in store for them.

Just outside the gate, Korczak, his mind on his cold wet feet and the ache that had already begun creeping to his ankles, found Comrade Bernard Goldstein, the socialist leader, at his side.

"He had no right to act as he did," Bernard hissed. "He was the only person in the ghetto whose voice carried authority. It was his duty to inform the people of the real state of affairs."

Korczak did not want to discuss the matter, but Bernard's vehemence demanded a reply, so he nodded his head in agreement, hoping to end the conversation.

"He should have dissolved all the public institutions," Bernard continued insistantly. "He was a coward!"

Korczak flushed with anger. "What does one man know of another's pain!" he said. "There is a limit to everyone's tolerance. He did what he thought he had to—and that took courage. At least he had the courage to act."

Both men mounted their bicycles. Korczak barely had the strength to pedal, and his bicycle began to wobble. Comrade Bernard rode alongside to steady him. There were tears in Korczak's eyes: his body had betrayed him. All of his life he had ridden bicycles, but now he hadn't strength enough even for that.

Goldstein wiped sweat from his face with his coat sleeve. "The time is coming when we must act, too, but not this way. We must strike back. Do you agree?"

"No," said Korczak who began to feel a little stronger. "There are just four possible ways of dealing with the Nazis. One: Bribery. Let them have the booty, then trick them. Two: Appear to agree with everything, then take the opportunity to carry out our own plans unobserved. We are alone, they are a pack. Three: Wait, consider, and watch, and at the right moment make a compromise. Four: Tire them out. Either they will go away or their attention will wander."

Comrade Bernard smiled. The scar received from a Russian saber when he was a sixteen-year-old revolutionary gave the smile a sinister appearance, but his words were good-humored. "Said like a true pedant. But perhaps we can convince you to join us. You have something at stake, you know: your own head plus your children's.

It won't hurt you to be exposed to our thinking. Perhaps we can benefit by yours. There is a meeting tomorrow morning in my apartment, Novolipya 12. Come. It may be worthwhile for everyone concerned."

11

Comrade Bernard's apartment at Novolipya 12 was well within the ghetto boundaries, and Korczak had been there before. The courtyard was a community center strewn with odds and ends of old furniture and other household possessions for which no room could be found indoors. In one corner bedding was hung to air; in another an old man worked patiently to fix a broken table. Women with pale, lifeless faces sat on the stone steps and sewed; others washed clothes, leaning over their wooden tubs; two held yellow-faced infants to their breasts. A

125

group of children danced in a circle, clapping their hands, singing a simple melody. Their attention was completely concentrated on a girl of fourteen or fifteen who led them in their play. Almost every courtyard had such "Kindergartens" since the Nazis had forbidden the Jews to have schools.

Korczak hurried past the polite greeting of the janitor and climbed up the narrow staircase to the first landing. This was packed with a dozen or more elderly people sitting on the stairs and listening to an old man teaching Yiddish to Jews who had gotten along without it all their lives, but who by German orders were strictly forbidden to speak Polish.

On the second landing he found a group of younger people discussing Polish literature. This "school" was doubly illegal, since the conversation was in Polish.

Korczak paused after the next flight to get his breath before knocking lightly on the door of the apartment. He was greeted by Comrade Bernard, who led him through the tiny entrance hallway to the kitchen in the front of the building.

"Berek saw you coming from the window," Comrade Bernard explained. "I don't open the door so quickly to everyone who knocks these days."

Three other men who had preceded him were sitting on packing cases, the only furniture in the room. Bernard took the case he had been sitting on and placed it lengthwise on the floor. He dusted it with a tattered handkerchief removed with a flourish from his pants pocket. "No bugs," he announced, beckoning Korczak to sit down.

Introductions were not necessary. Korczak was acquainted with the other men and knew them to be realists as well as dedicated Socialists. There was Berek Snaidmil, thin and wiry, sitting tensely by the cardboard-covered window. After acknowledging Korczak with a nod, he continued to study the street below.

The second member of the group was Abrasha Blum. Tall, slim, quiet, with eyeglasses and thinning hair, he looked more like an intellectual than a military commander. Korczak knew that Abrasha suffered severely from a chronic stomach ailment; he had treated him often.

The third man was fifty-year-old Morizi Orzech, writer and editor. He had left Warsaw for Kaunas at the outbreak of the war. The Germans demanded that the Lithuanian government surrender him because of a sizzling dispatch he had written to the *Jewish Daily Forward* in New York City, detailing Nazi treatment of Jews in occupied areas.

He was brought to the frontier and saved at the last moment, only to be arrested at sea aboard a neutral ship and sent to a German camp for Polish prisoners of war.

The Germans soon began sorting out all Jews from among their Polish military prisoners, returning them to their homes in accordance with the long-range plan for total extermination. Among the first was Orzech. In contrast with "old-fashioned" Socialists, whose disregard for fashion was part of their revolt against convention, Morizi was always neatly dressed. Even during these desperate times his worn suit was pressed and, Korczak noted with approval, his shoes were shined.

Comrade Bernard was not a man to waste words. "We

have a problem, Henryk," he said, using the doctor's given name.

"When you say 'we' are you speaking as a Socialist, a Jew, or a Pole?" asked Korczak.

"When I say 'we' I mean everyone in the ghetto," said Comrade Bernard patiently. "The Germans are determined to exterminate all Jews. It is only a matter of time before the Warsaw ghetto and its Jews will be only a bitter memory in the world."

Korczak felt his muscles stiffen. It seemed obvious that Comrade Bernard knew something, and he wasn't certain he wanted to be given the information. He raised his hand halfheartedly as if to protest, but Bernard was determined to continue. "Hear me out," he said. "The evidence is clear: the Jews who have been plucked from the streets and supposedly sent to labor camps for resettlement; they never get to the East."

Korczak lifted his hands to his face. He was beginning to perspire. "But I've had cards from friends," he said.

"We've all had cards," interrupted Bernard. "And the cards are all worded alike. We've compared them. They say the same thing. They have identical postmarks."

"That doesn't prove anything," said Korczak.

"True," said Bernard. "But Abrasha has found out something which does prove something."

Abrasha coughed self-consciously. "I have a cousin," he said. "He's a policeman; he works at the Umschlagplatz. Before that, before the Nazis, he was a journalist. He has a very orderly mind. He's a very methodical man. He got bored loading people into boxcars, so, as a game, he started memorizing the numbers on the cars.

"One day he noticed that the cars he had helped load that morning were back at the siding in the afternoon. He thought he had made a mistake. So he wrote down the numbers the next day. The next afternoon, the cars were back.

"Then he thought that perhaps the cars had similar numbers, so he started to put a little X next to the locks after he had sealed them, and then he wrote down the numbers. Several of these cars were back that same afternoon."

Comrade Bernard interrupted.

"It takes a train at least twenty hours to go to the Russian border on the Bialystok-Minsk line from Warsaw," he said heavily, "But it took only six hours for the cars carrying Jews to the East to make the round trip."

Korczak was breathing rapidly, almost gasping, as if he had been climbing a mountain.

"Well, what do you think now?" asked Bernard.

"I don't know," said Korczak.

"You don't know because you don't want to know," said Bernard, "You're like the rest of the Jews here in the ghetto; you don't believe that a German, even one wearing the uniform of the SS, can renounce his humanity and murder tens of thousands of people in cold blood.

"You still believe that the fatherland of Kant, Goethe, and Beethoven cannot be a nation of murderers. You won't believe it until your time comes; until you too die— with your children. But I tell you, there is no doubt about it: we Jews are being exterminated, swiftly and surely."

Korczak made a gesture of resignation. "If what you say is true, what then?" he asked.

"We must persuade the ghetto to revolt, to die fighting, if we must die. Will you join us if we get absolute proof that the Jews are being annihilated? Will you write for us and help us persuade the others when the time comes to revolt?"

Korczak considered for only a moment, then nodded firmly. "Yes," he said.

Bernard's face brightened, and there was a note of authority in his voice. "I want you to get hold of Zygmunt Friedrych," he told Blum. "Tell him I want to see him as soon as possible."

"What are you planning?" Korczak asked.

"I want to smuggle Friedrych out of the ghetto to try and discover where the deportation trains are going. If things are as we suspect, he'll bring back the proof we need to convince every single Jew in the ghetto to revolt."

"Do you think Friedrych has a chance to accomplish this?"

Bernard thought a moment. Zygmunt Friedrych was one of the most daring individuals in the underground. He was a strong, handsome young man whose wife and daughter lived in safety with Aryans on the other side of the wall. Most important, he looked like a pure Aryan, an invaluable asset for a Jew traveling outside the ghetto walls.

"Yes," Bernard finally said. "I think he has a chance."

12

The Bund assigned Adziu to lead Zygmunt Friedrych out of the ghetto so he could determine what was actually happening to the trainloads of Jews being shipped out of Warsaw.

The safest route was underground, through the sewer system which spread beneath all of Warsaw like a foul labyrinth. Its huge main arteries crisscrossed smaller tributaries in a nightmare of black confusion, and throughout the entire network the accumulated filth of the great city sloshed.

131

To crawl through the sewers without a thorough knowledge of their geography could mean death by suffocation or drowning. But to Adziu the sewers were like a kindergarten playground. He had learned the most expeditious and safest routes while working for Bala Schulz as a smuggler. Now the Bund was putting his knowledge to work.

It was past curfew time when Friedrych met Adziu at their predetermined rendezvous. The streets were empty. There was not a light anywhere; even the July moon was ghostly pale. Except for the footsteps of occasional patrols one would have thought the ghetto completely deserted.

Friedrych knew Adziu was one of Korczak's orphans. After the two shook hands, Friedrych whispered, "How are things at the orphanage?"

Adziu shrugged. "We survive," he said noncommittally. Then he added, "Do not worry about the sewers. I know them well."

Adziu moved off into the shadows. Friedrych followed him closely. The boy was surefooted and quiet as a cat. He clung to the sides of buildings, melted into doorways, sneaked through alleys where he knew exactly which boards to lift to allow them to squeeze through.

At the corner of Leszno and Karmelicka Streets they paused. Adziu waved into the darkness. Friedrych assumed a signal was given in return because Adziu hastened up Leszno, hugging the building fronts. They stopped again in the doorway of a leather tannery.

"We have to wait for another signal," Adziu whispered.

Finally it came. There was a tremendous clatter behind them on Karmelicka that sounded like a huge column of cans being upended.

"Get ready," Adziu hissed.

A squad of Ukranians patrolling farther up Leszno trotted right by them, guns at the ready. As the squad rounded the corner of Karmelicka, Adziu tugged at Friedrych's coat and ran to a manhole cover in the middle of the road. Friedrych followed him. He watched how quickly and expertly the boy inserted a small piece of metal under the lip of the cover, the ease with which he lifted the heavy lid from its recess and slid it quietly back on the cobblestone pavement.

Adziu stepped aside and impatiently waved Friedrych into the hole. As Friedrych climbed awkwardly down the slimy ladder he heard the squeal of rats. Then he felt the cold, filthy sewage oozing up his pants legs and into his shoes. The odor hit him suddenly, and he gagged.

After replacing the cover, Adziu slid down next to Friedrych. "You will have to crawl behind me through this first section," he whispered. "Keep your face close to the water. The gas is not so bad there. If you have to vomit, do it quietly. I will wait for you."

The boy knelt. Friedrych followed suit. They entered a tunnel about twenty inches high and wide enough for only one person to crawl through. Friedrych's head and shoulders scraped against the overhead. A claustrophobic panic rose in him. He stuffed the tail of Adziu's shirt in his mouth and bit down hard. This way he could use both his hands to support himself and still be assured that he would not be left behind. Biting the material helped ease his anxiety. It did nothing to still the waves of nausea in his stomach.

Friedrych would never forget the next forty minutes. He kept his face as close to the fetid waters as he could.

Twice he slipped, and the foul liquid entered his nose and trickled down his throat. Twice he had to tug violently at Adziu's shirt to make him stop while he backed off, vomited, then crawled forward to catch up with the boy again.

Several times they came to sewer junctions, but Adziu unhesitatingly directed their course. At one point they emerged from the narrow tunnels and slipped chest-deep into the rushing waters of a main sewer. Although he could not see them, Friedrych's flesh crawled as he heard rats swim past his face in the darkness. The poisonous fumes were heavier here, and he almost panicked when he realized he was getting weak and dizzy.

Finally they stopped. Friedrych could see a few pinpoints of light overhead.

"We are here," Adziu whispered. He tugged and pushed Friedrych out of the stream and against one wall. Then the boy placed Friedrych's hands on a ladder and whispered a hardly audible "Good luck."

Friedrych straightened up and slowly climbed the ladder. When he was able to reach the manhole cover, he pushed against it just enough to lift it a few inches. The cool night air rushed cleanly into his lungs. He stood there breathing heavily for a moment, then peered out. He saw that he was in a park and there was no one in sight, but he had to make sure. He lowered the cover and lifted its opposite lip. He was less than twenty feet from a fountain. He recognized it. He was in Saxon Park on the Aryan side of Warsaw.

Three times more Friedrych peered periscope-like from beneath the manhole cover before he was satisfied that there was no one in sight. Then he climbed out of the sewer. He was only a few hundred yards from the ghetto wall which was screened from his sight by trees. Behind him, Adziu was already sliding the lid back into place. In a moment the slight rasping noise stopped and Adziu was gone.

Friedrych started walking. He knew Saxon Park well. Like most Warsaw children, he had grown up among its trees, fountains, flower beds, statues, bandstands, and the beautiful colonnaded buildings which surrounded it. Even in his haste from long habit he avoided stepping on the grassy areas marked "No Walking."

The smell of the sewer still clogged his nostrils as he emerged into the city. He breathed only through his mouth. With every step his shoes squished ooze. He headed directly for the bank of the Vistula. The first thing he had to do was to clean out his shoes and wash his clothes.

There was light traffic on the river: a few barges and ships carrying supplies. It was still too dark for him to make out distinct shapes. He disrobed entirely and shivered while he rinsed and wrung out his clothes a dozen times. He thought of Adziu with the ferret's face and wondered how long it had taken him to get used to the awful environment of the sewers.

Kneeling in some tall grass, Friedrych wrung out his clothes for the last time. The tainted odor of the sewers still clung to them. He rubbed them with handfuls of green grass for a few moments, then dressed and started out.

Fearing he would meet a German patrol, Friedrych

avoided the footpath along the Vistula and chose instead to walk along the uneven riverbank until he came to a bridge. He clambered across the bridge on the narrow trestles beneath the roadway, shivering from cold and fear. He was well aware that he was clearly visible and made a good target from the other side, but the crossing was without incident.

Now he followed the arcing railroad tracks and walked through Praga with its prosperous homes and yards overflowing with beautiful flowers. In the distance he saw the ragged silhouettes of buildings gutted by the battle for Warsaw. The sight registered dully on his mind. He was amazed at how much clearer and cleaner the air was on this, "the other side."

It was as though nature, too, shunned the ghetto.

A Polish Socialist, a railroad worker, knew the direction taken by the deportation trains and had advised Friedrych to follow the line to Solokov. He had also given him an address in Solokov where he could get further directions. Because of his Aryan looks, Friedrych had been told to walk alongside the tracks. He had a card that identified him as a railroad laborer. If stopped he was to say that he was checking the rails, a legitimate job.

Pushing his strong body to the limit, Friedrych put thirty kilometers between himself and Warsaw before midday of the twenty-third. By that time his clothes had dried, and he had regained his appetite. He ate a chunk of bread and munched on a dried apple while squatting on one of the rails.

His brief lunch was interrupted by vibrations he felt on the tracks. A train was on its way. Springing to the side of the railroad bed, he clambered up a small incline and hid behind some brush. The tracks were below him now, and as the train came near he heard a strange moaning. It was an eerie, hopeless wail, spilling down the tracks like the mounting surge of an incoming tide. He began sweating with horror the moment he realized that the moaning was coming from one of the convoys of deportees.

The train, forty-five cattle cars long, rolled by, and he saw grotesque grimaces on faces of people packed inside as they pressed against the grates at the top of the cars. More than that, he could actually smell the bodies, and the odor to him was worse than that of the sewers. He lost the little lunch he had eaten. Even after the train had passed he could hear the moaning following it like a dirge.

A few kilometers from Sokolov he saw armed guards patrolling a roadway over a bridge. He assumed they were soldiers on the lookout for saboteurs. Rather than risk being stopped and interrogated he decided to make a long detour through the countryside.

It was dark when Friedrych arrived in Sokolov. He had a map directing him to the place he was to meet the Socialist who would be expecting him. The streets were deserted, and Friedrych had no trouble locating the address encircled on his map.

Friedrych had started climbing the steps into the building before he realized with horror that he was walking into a police station. He quickly checked the address again. It was the right building. He went in cautiously, rigid with fear. A single, green-shaded lamp burned above a scarred desk in the large room. Behind the desk, his face shadowed ominously by the yellow-green light, a Polish policeman sat staring at Friedrych. After studying Friedrych for a long moment, the man spoke one word.

"Friedrych?"

Friedrych nodded with relief.

"Good," said the policeman. "I am the only one on duty at night. We are alone." Then he added, as if trying to make a joke, "Where could we Socialists find a safer place to meet than in a police station?"

Friedrych did not laugh. He half-collapsed into a chair opposite the desk, and listened intently while the policeman, speaking quietly, told Friedrych that the Germans had built a small branch railroad to the village of Treblinka. "Each day the trains packed with Jews are switched onto this new spur," he said. "We know that Treblinka itself is a large camp divided into two sections: one for Jews and one for Poles, and we hear that terrible things are happening there. But we have no precise information."

"Can't you get it?" Friedrych asked him.

"No," the policeman replied. "No one can get close enough to Treblinka. It is too heavily guarded with soldiers and dogs."

"Is there no way at all to find out what is happening there?" Friedrych asked.

"Perhaps," the policeman said. "There is a farmer here in Sokolov who is hiding an escapee from Treblinka. I tried to get the poor devil to talk to me, but he will speak only to another Jew."

138

"Take me to him," Friedrych said as he stood up. "He will speak to me."

The policeman reached into his pocket and handed Friedrych an address. "It would be better if you went yourself. I will wait for you here."

Friedrych took the address. "What is the man's name?" he asked.

"He refused to give it. A precaution against the Germans taking reprisals against his family in case he is captured. But he has long since ceased being a name anyway. Ask for him by his number: Katzetnick 12973."

Friedrych walked briskly and in a few minutes arrived at the farmhouse where the escapee from Treblinka was being hidden. He knocked at the door. A tall, thin man opened the door a crack and glared suspiciously at Friedrych through eyes that were set too close together in a lined face.

"What do you want?"

"I was told you have Katzetnick 12973 here. I want to speak with him."

"Who are you?"

"That is not important. I will give you one thousand zlotys if you let me speak to him."

The farmer looked at Friedrych and said, "You'll get nothing from him. He'll only talk to another Jew."

"I am a Jew," Friedrych said.

The farmer wiped at his mouth. "I didn't go through all the trouble of hiding him here and nursing his wound for a stinking one thousand zlotys. I can sell him to the Germans for ten times that. You Jews will have to come up with more money if you want him."

Friedrych felt rage surge up inside him but restrained himself. Obviously the man had helped the prisoner only to sell him later to the highest bidder. It mattered little to the farmer whether that bidder was German or Jew.

"I don't want to buy the man from you," Friedrych said. "The one thousand zlotys is just to talk to him." He reached into his pocket and waved the money, all he had, in front of the farmer. Then, suspecting the man might try to collect the reward for two Jews while he was talking to the escapee, he added, "You can sit with us to make sure I do not try to sneak off with him."

The farmer grumbled but took the money and led Friedrych inside the house and into a small room whose one window was covered with brown sacking. The farmer closed the door behind them, pulled a chair in front of it, and sat down. It took Friedrych a moment to get used to the gloom, but then he saw the still form of a man asleep on a straw cot in the corner of the room. He walked to the cot, drew up a stool, and sat down. The man's back was toward him. He touched his bony shoulder. Startled, Katzetnick 12973 jerked his face toward Friedrych. Friedrych was not prepared for the sight and smell that greeted him. The man's lower jay was a mass of suppurating, gangrenous tissue, and the odor pouring from it was vile beyond description.

Friedrych recoiled involuntarily but quickly controlled himself. He leaned forward, put his hand gently on the man's forehead, and told him that he was a Jew, had come from the ghetto in Warsaw where the people were desperately waiting to learn what fate was befalling the Jews at Treblinka.

140

Katzetnick 12973 seized Freidrych's hand and, pressing it, moaned, "Thank God! Thank God!" Then, after sobbing for a moment, he drew Friedrych's face close to his own and said in a weak, hardly audible whisper, "Tell them what is happening there. I have kept myself alive just so that they should know what is happening to us."

Friedrych put his ear near Katzetnick 12973's mouth and with the sickening odor of the man's wound fuming at his nostrils he listened to his story.

"I was a mason in Warsaw before the Germans came. A good one," he began. "They needed men who could lay brick, mix concrete, and read blueprints, so they let me work when they took me prisoner, let me stay alive as best I could."

Stopping only to catch his breath and cough occasionally, Katzetnick 12973 went on to tell Friedrych that he had been sent to Treblinka B in May 1941. It was a camp on the site of a gravel pit near the Warsaw-Bialystok railroad line, a few kilometers from Malkinia in a sandy, wooded area. The camp was comparatively small, about 12,500 acres. It was entirely surrounded by a green fence interwoven with barbed-wire entanglements. Part of the fence ran through a young forest in the north. At the four corners of the camp, observation posts were placed for the Lagerschutz, the Camp Guard. The Lagerschutz consisted mostly of Ukranians armed with machine guns. They also operated the powerful searchlights mounted on the observation posts which lit the entire camp at night.

Friedrych learned that there were observation posts in the middle of the camp and on the hills in the woodlands, and that a railroad embankment formed the western border of Treblinka B. "It is along this embankment," Katzetnick 12973 whispered, "that a side track connecting the camp with the main railroad line runs. This is so that they can deliver the transports directly to Treblinka B, which they converted from a concentration camp to an extermination camp."

Friedrych started. "Then it is true?"

Katzetnick 12973 nodded. He was getting weaker, but by an effort of will he kept talking.

"For three months I helped them build the gas chamber at Treblinka B. It was not a shoddy structure, but solid, well engineered. You know the Germans.

"It has three white-walled rooms built to look like shower rooms. Each room is about two meters high and twenty-five square meters in area. A narrow corridor fronts all three of them. That's where they ran the pipes and valves. Outside, ventilators, the kind you see on ships . . . power room at one end . . . doors, scoops, and valves, everything sealed hermetically. The floors get very slippery when they're wet . . . white tiles."

It was strange for Friedrych to hear this man speaking of structural details, but he did not interrupt him. For some reason they were important to Katzetnick 12973.

Suddenly Katzetnick 12973 squeezed Friedrych's hand. "You don't blame me for working on the gas chambers, do you?" he said anxiously.

"Of course not," Friedrych said softly. "You had to."

The farmer squirmed in his chair. He had been listening to everything. "I was wondering how he managed to stay alive in there," he said aloud.

"Shut up!" Friedrych growled.

Katzetnick 12973 continued. There was a different note

to his whisperings. It was lower, more rasping, and he spoke with great emotion, as if trying to purge himself of an overwhelming guilt. He also began to shiver at this point, wildly, uncontrollably. Then the stark horror of his tale came out.

"The first convoy of Jews from Warsaw arrived on July twenty-fourth. It was twenty cars. Since then two transports a day, one in the morning and one in the afternoon. Forty or more freight cars in each one of them. They pull some of the cars onto a siding across from the arrival square. The others are shifted to another track to wait their turn.

"More than a hundred Jews are packed in each car. And the Germans coat the floors of the cars with lime so that the people breathe a sigh of relief when they are let out on the square. It is all planned . . . it is all planned."

Friedrych began stroking Katzetnick 12973's hair in an effort to quiet the man's shivering. He continued stroking it even though it did not help.

"Then the Kapos take over, Jewish auxiliary guards. The women and children are told to enter the barracks while the men remain in the square. There is a poster in the square that says, 'Attention Natives of Warsaw. Do not worry about your fate. You are all going eastward for work. You will work and your wives will take care of your households. Before leaving, however, you have to take a bath and your clothing must be disinfected. You have to deposit your valuables and money with the cashier for which you will get receipts. After the bath and disinfection you will receive everything back unharmed.' That's what the sign says. That's exactly what it says.

"Then a kind-looking SS officer comes to the square

and gives a speech along the same lines. They do it to build up the people's confidence that nothing is going to happen to them. After that the Kapos line the men up in rows of ten and make everyone take off his shoes, undress naked, and prepare for the bath. And everybody does it. No one questions because they let them take soap with them and their documents. And while the men stand their, naked, in line, the sorting-service men come and take their clothes to the sorting place. And at the same time, the women and children are also made to undress completely."

Katzetnick 12973 suddenly let out a moan which dissolved into a hacking cough that shook the cot.

"He's not going to die on me, is he?" the farmer asked, leaning forward anxiously. "He's no good to me dead. Come on. You've talked enough for the one thousand zlotys."

The farmer made a move to seize Friedrych's arm. Friedrych glared once at him, and the farmer sullenly retreated to his chair.

Katzetnick 12973 coughed for a full minute. Friedrych sat and watched him, amazed that the man could still be alive, let alone talk coherently. Obviously the only thing keeping him going was his feverish will to survive long enough to tell his story, to warn Poland's Jews of the fate that awaited them at Treblinka.

When Katzetnick 12973 was able to speak again, there was a new sound in his throat, a rattle behind every whispered word, a rattle Friedrych knew was death.

"The women line up naked with the children and enter the 'shower rooms,' " Katzetnick 12973 went on, slowly,

144

painfully. "The chief himself stands in front of death house Number One. He is never without his whip. Then the Germans with their whips and clubs beat the women and children into the house as fast as they can.

"I told you the floors of the chambers were slippery. The women slip and fall and cannot stand because others are driven in right on top of them. The chief picks up small children and throws them into the chambers over the heads of the women. Then they seal the doors hermetically and suffocate everyone inside with the steam they let out of the pipe vents. In the beginning you can hear the women and the children screaming. It takes fifteen minutes for the silence to come. That is what the Germans mean when they say 'resettlement.' Resettlement is when the Jews are all dead."

Friedrych sat trying to fight down his own tears and rage as Katzetnick 12973 went on to tell him about the gravediggers.

"The German overseers drive the diggers to their work. Part of their job is to get the dead bodies out of the execution chambers. When the doors open, not a body falls out of the chambers. All the women and children stick together. It is like a solid block of arms, legs, and bodies."

Friedrych shuddered. His stomach heaved, but there was nothing in it to be brought up. He swallowed hard a few times while Katzetnick 12973 continued.

"The diggers have to pour cold well water over the bodies to separate them. And while they are doing this, the Germans are beating and cursing to hurry them. By the time the chambers are empty, the bodies are piled up

145

on carts, like slaughtered cattle. Then the diggers—they are all Jews—take the bodies to the ditches. They have to push their carts at a run so the burial can take place quickly. For that reason, too, the graves are dug near the death house. As new bodies are added, the grave line is moved farther and farther east. Then, after the grave is filled with bodies, the diggers shovel dirt over the dead while the digging machine prepares the next grave."

"Why is there no rioting?" Friedrych asked.

"Because it is all too sudden, too carefully planned. No one knows until it is too late that they are going to their death."

"But what about the men?"

"The men are executed the same way the women are. They have no time to organize a riot. They are driven through the woods to the chambers and it is all over before they can even think of doing anything."

"Do you mean that no one knows?"

"Once in a while the chambers are overcrowded and the Germans are forced to keep some of them standing in the woods near the slaughterhouse. These people see and hear everything. But even they do not riot. It is difficult to riot when you are standing barefoot and naked with guns pointed at you."

The muscles in Friedrych's body were so tense by now that he started quaking with anger and frustration.

"The new death house I was working on before I escaped was designed to handle eight thousand victims a day," Katzetnick 12973 groaned. "They have it ready for use now."

"God! God! God" Friedrych croaked. He clenched his

fists and pounded his forehead. "And you are the only one who escaped?" he asked.

Katzetnick 12973 nodded. "While I was working on the gas chambers, seven transports arrived from Warsaw. I was scheduled to die in the eighth group, but there was a failure in the ventilators. I was among eight hundred men they marched outside the camp and forced to dig a mass grave. They lined us up in groups of fifty in front of the grave. I was in the last group. I stood there and watched while Germans walked behind the men and shot each one behind the ear. I was crazy with fear. All I wanted was the nearest German to hurry so that he could get to me right away.

"When my time finally came, I must have moved my head at the same time he pulled the trigger. The force of the bullet knocked me into the grave. The smell made me realize I was still alive. I was lying on top of eight hundred dead men. Each one had defecated the moment he died."

Friedrych could see where the bullet had entered Katzetnick 12973's neck, furrowed along his jawbone, and come out at his chin. He shuddered at the pain the man must have been feeling as he moved his mouth to speak.

By this time Katzetnick 12973 was almost totally spent. But he gave Friedrych the last details of his story. He told him, pausing between words to catch his breath, how the mass execution had not been completed until night had fallen. The Germans had not wanted to light up the area outside of camp for a burial detail and instead had simply posted a guard there. The soldiers had started playing cards after a time, and Katzetnick 12973 had dragged himself over the heap of bodies and into the woods. Somehow he had managed to crawl to the main road where the farmer, passing by in his hay wagon, had discovered him.

Glancing toward the farmer, who was still sitting at the door to the room, Katzetnick 12973 twisted his face into a tortured smile. "He plans," he gasped in Yiddish to Friedrych, "to claim a reward for me. I think he will be disappointed."

Friedrych understood. The man knew he would be dead before the farmer could collect a bounty for him.

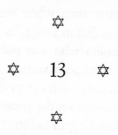

13

German headquarters for the administration of the
ghetto was a former military prison at the corner of
Gensia and Zamenhofa. SS guards carrying machine
pistols patrolled the barbed-wire barrier in front. The
building itself had been carefully fortified: ground-floor
windows had steel shutters, to prevent grenades or Molotov cocktails being tossed in, and there were armor-plated
turrets housing light machine guns on the roof.

The leaders of the ghetto underground chose an apartment directly across the street for their most important

meeting on the theory that the Germans would never suspect subversive activities right under their noses. The proximity of the SS was on everyone's mind on the afternoon of July 29 when a meeting of the eighteen underground groups active in the ghetto was scheduled.

"This is even better than when we met in the cellar under the officers' brothel in Praga," a young Bundist said to his older companion who was puffing and wheezing for breath as they climbed a vertical ladder joining two attics. Holes had secretly been cut in the walls of attics of the big apartment houses on the principal streets to allow passageway from building to building. These attic routes enabled Jews to travel through the ghetto with minimal exposure to the dangerous streets.

Other representatives from the underground groups urgently summoned to the meeting had been coming to the apartment through a tunnel which connected the cellars of several buildings. Only a few of the very old men, including two rabbis from the Agudah Council, risked coming through the street entrance.

This was the second time in a week that some of the men had met. A July 23 convocation of underground leaders had broken up when the majority voted against an immediate resistance, arguing that it would serve as an excuse for a total massacre. "Painful as it is," they argued, "it is better to sacrifice seventy thousand Jews destined for deportation than to endanger the lives of half of million. Since the Nazis apply the principle of collective responsibility, a struggle would bring disaster to all."

That argument carried the day, since no one was certain that deportation meant death. Friedrych's report in the second edition of "Oif der Wach" was the first eyewitness account published in any of the ghetto's forty-three underground newspapers. It was so full of convincing detail that although most Jews refused to believe it, the majority of the representatives meeting on this day were convinced of its accuracy.

Despite their desperate situation, there was a formal politeness, carried over from gentler days, between the participants. "If I may remind the honorable representative of the Bund, the report in 'Oif der Wach' has not been confirmed," said a rabbi from the Agudah Council. "We cannot start an insurrection that might cost us all our lives because of one report. Until I see it for myself I will not believe it."

"It will be too late then, my friend," said Comrade Bernard.

"It is never too late, my esteemed Comrade Bernard," said the rabbi.

"We have already covered this ground," said Bernard. "The meeting was called today because we have proof the Germans intend to murder us all."

There was a murmur of assent from the men who filled the small room, either sitting on the floor or leaning against the walls. A young representative from Gordonia was stationed by the window watching the street and the German Headquarters for signs of unusual activity.

The discussion, always in muffled tones or rasping whispers, was long and hectic. The Zionists wanted to evacuate the Jews to Palestine. The Bund wanted to know how the Zionists would get the Jews out of the ghetto and into Palestine, a question the Zionists could not answer.

151

There was a proposal that a courier be sent to Switzerland to meet with the representative of international Jewry there and urge him to prevail upon Great Britain immediately to recognize all Jews as citizens of Palestine.

A rabbi seconded the suggestion. "Our whole life is turned toward the land of Israel," he said. "It is only an accident that we are still in exile. We have been brought up to work and fight in the land of Israel, not here. The only future of the Jewish peoples is in the land of Israel, and it is by building a nation there that we will save our people, not sacrificing them here in useless combat."

Someone suggested attempting to bribe Hoeffle, an idea that drew a contemptuous chorus of whispers. The representative from the Misrachi was sneered at when, on "unimpeachable information," he claimed the Germans were being truthful when they said they wanted only seventy thousand Jews for labor.

Despite the opposition of the rabbis it was apparent the majority recognized the need for armed resistance. The Bund favored such a course, but Comrade Bernard made it clear that the Bund would not join formally with the other organizations, although they would fight the Germans with all their resources. Comrade Bernard felt the ghetto branch of the Bund should move in concert with the Polish Socialist Party outside the ghetto, and he expected orders soon to begin a coordinated battle.

The meeting was deathly still for a moment following Comrade Bernard's announcement. He shifted uneasily, knowing that most of the delegates had been counting on the Bund to lead them into battle.

The delegate from Hashomer broke the silence by

152

firmly announcing, "We are sorry to hear this from our friend of the Bund. It is time nevertheless to go ahead, with or without the Polish Socialists, although of course," with a nod to Comrade Bernard, "we prefer to have them with us. But for some time we of Hashomer have had in preparation a table of organization."

In a matter of minutes the Jewish Fighting Organization came into being, embracing all the groups present except the Bund. The Bund would battle as a separate unit but coordinate all activities with the organization.

As a gesture of cooperation Comrade Bernard offered to contribute his entire arsenal to the newly formed committee. He reached into his pocket and dropped onto the table an old German Army Luger, a gift from the Polish Worker's Party. And so the official Jewish resistance against the Nazis began.

14

It was 2:00 A.M. and on this hot July night Korczak felt his strength ebbing. His knees were shaky, his pulse weak. He sat down to read and his vision blurred. The lines became wavy and seemed to slide together, leaving white gaps as if the text had disappeared in some mysterious way. The heat was unbearable, flowing down directly from the ceiling over his head.

Several times he walked the twenty paces to the front door, thrusting his head out into the comparative coolness. He stood there so long his knees became weak, his legs weightless. He grasped the door frame with both hands, afraid he would lose his footing.

But he stayed at the doorway as long as he could because from it he could see two worlds. Above him were the heavens, thickly strewn with stars. When he looked up he became aware of that infinite extension which is, according to Spinoza, one of God's attributes. And he mused on a subject which had puzzled him, with which he struggled to get into some kind of bearable perspective: the strange relationships of time and space. At a previous point in time he had been busy with his children and his writing. The world was available: he could go out into it, or it came to him in the form of visitors, movies, newspapers, and radio. He was the same human being as he had been three years earlier, but now that life, the world, seemed as remote as the stars above the ghetto.

Yet for almost everyone else the world continued on its course. Less than two miles away on the Polish farms, or five thousand miles away in New York, the overwhelming plurality of human beings were sleeping or eating or working or making love. And this is where his imagination balked. The two orders of simultaneous experience were so different, so irreconcilable, and their coexistence such a hideous paradox.

After a fourth visit to the door he bolted it and lay on his cot. Although he was exhausted, he could not sleep. It had been a particularly trying day. The authorities had ordered the evacuation of Stawka Hospital and had sent only the serious cases to the hospital at Zelazna. There had still been 170 sickly children to be accounted for, and the Jewish Communal Council had decided that half of the group be sent to him. There were fifteen other homes in the area, but his was the nearest.

He had spent the entire day trying to find room at Our Home for eighty-five frightened and despairing new children, many of whom were feverish. There had been no room, but somehow he made some. He had doubled those who were not ill into beds with children already in the orphanage. He had squeezed extra cots into the boy's dormitory and put the sick children there. There were six more cots in his own room, making a total of nine children who shared his cramped quarters with him. As he lay there listening to their fitful breathing, a pang of guilt over a feeling he had had that afternoon flowed through his aching body.

He had not felt kindly toward the new children when they had been thrust upon him; to be honest, he had considered them invaders. More than once during the day he had caught himself thinking that he would not give them whole spoonfuls of cod-liver oil, that they were made of such base stuff that no flowers or useful green things would grow on their graves, only thistles and weeds. It did not matter that in the end he had given each new child a spoonful and had tried to make them comfortable. He had felt resentment, and that made him ashamed.

In the girl's dormitory a child cried out in her sleep. Korczak tried to guess who it was. But she quieted, and he shifted on his cot and tried again to fall asleep. He could not, but thought instead of the two times that day he had snapped at Miss Hannia, the nurse at the orphanage.

"Smile," he had said. "Make jokes."

"I am too tired," she had answered him.

"I am tired too," he had said. "But how do you expect to keep the children happy if you do not make jokes with them?"

Later in the day he sent her for some bedclothes for a feverish child. She had been away a long time and when she had returned he snapped, "Did you enjoy your stroll?"

"I am not quick like you," she had said. "There are just too many children to care for . . . and I need sleep."

"I sleep as little as you do," he had said. "But I am quick on my feet because I am still alive and fighting. We must be quick if we are to survive."

It was quiet outside, Korczak thought, like the hollow silence of a deep well. Suddenly, shattering the stillness like a rock dropped into the well, he heard the clatter of a patrol running by. Then an ominous quiet again.

He was almost asleep when he heard a quiet but persistent knocking on the front door. It would not be a patrol—they would have pounded. Perhaps it was someone seeking a hiding place, or Adziu with the Germans at his heels.

Cautiously he threaded his way through the maze of cots in his room, then slipped on his green smock and started for the door. He padded barefoot down the corridor, slid the bolt back on the door, and drew it open about four inches, enough to enable him to peer out into the street. In the blackness he could make out a man's shape near the door, and out in the street he had an impression rather than a view of a squad of soldiers. "Who's there?" he asked in a whisper.

157

The man near the door spoke to him in German. "Untersturmfuehrer Schneider."

The name meant nothing to Korczak. "What can I do for you, Lieutenant?" he asked.

"Herr Doktor, it is Erwin. Erwin Schneider."

The name was vaguely familiar to Korczak. He could not associate it with a face, but obviously it should mean something to him from the way it was given. He opened the door, and a young German lieutenant entered.

"Where can we talk?" asked the lieutenant, as he waved the patrol off on its rounds.

"The only room in the house that is not crowded with children is the W.C." said Korczak.

"Lead the way," Schneider ordered.

Korczak, followed by the lieutenant, padded down the dark entrance corridor to the W.C. installed by the Guild of Merchants. He fumbled with the bolt and opened the door. The smell of ammonia was overpowering. There were two urinals—two open holes in the tile floor with grab handles at the sides. There was a wooden bench opposite. The one window was sandbagged because it was on the ground floor. Korczak pushed a bag loose to allow some light and air in. A trickle of moonlight outlined the silhouettes of the two men. The lieutenant joined Korczak at the window.

"You still do not remember me, do you?" asked the lieutenant.

Korczak put his hand to his temple and shook his head. "I am still sleepy, Lieutenant," he said. "You must forgive me. Should I know you?"

"You knew me as a boy," Erwin prompted. "As Erwin Schneider at the orphanage on Cedrowa Street."

"Yes. Yes. Of course," Korczak said. He was about to place his hand on Erwin's knee in a warm gesture of recognition, but the SS uniform stopped him. Instead he pointed at the toilets and said, "The little German boy with the W.C. tax. For a thin stool, five flies, for a thick one, ten. For a first-class stool, fifteen. Soon you had all the boys catching flies."

"That's right," Erwin said and smiled, but only briefly. His mouth tightened, and he indicated that he was ready to get down to the business at hand.

"I gather that this is not a social visit," Korczak said.

"No it is not, Herr Doktor," Erwin said.

Korczak studied Erwin, who started pacing back and forth while a flow of carefully chosen words, obviously a speech he had taken pains to prepare, poured stiffly from him.

". . . and it is not an issue which you can dodge by simply turning your back on it and refusing to face the reality of the situation. You must realize that you and I and all your children alike bear specific responsibilities under the New Order. We are obliged, whether we like it or not, to aid and not obstruct the dynamic and inevitable movement toward the establishment of order within the framework of our . . . new . . . society . . ."

Erwin droned on, his words reaching Korczak's consciousness like the recurring waves of a dull toothache. "So," Korczak mused, the full impact of his weariness settling painfully in his body, "they have sent a boy to me out of another age to tempt me with the innocence of what he once was. Look at him in his black soldier's suit. Corrupted, conditioned. He is no longer one of my boys. He is a puppet, a Judas goat sent to lure me to the slaughter. What must they take me for?"

". . . and it is not an easy task for us. Do you realize the staggering problems we face in logistics alone?" Erwin said and stopped pacing. "To efficiently move such a mass of people from point A to point B requires a titanic amount of precise planning and effort."

Korczak nodded. He seemed attentive, and Erwin continued outlining his argument. Korczak, however, hardly heard a word he was saying. He was remembering a day long ago when he had stood watching a soccer game. He had had his arm around Erwin's shoulders. They were standing at the sidelines and Erwin was close to tears because he had not been chosen on either team.

Again, Korczak focused on Erwin. He tried to keep his mind on what he was saying, but he was tired and longed for the soft warmth of his bed.

". . . but we Germans are not playing at war," Erwin was saying as he propped his foot up on the bench. "We are waging it quickly and thoroughly. We are the iron plow turning the soil, clearing the weeds and planting the grain. Tomorrow there will be flour and bread. But first there must be order. Trains run according to a timetable which has to be arranged in advance. Nothing must interfere with our schedule."

Just then the door rattled slightly. Korczak stood. "Excuse me, Lieutenant," he said and went to the door. A young boy, a newcomer barely five, stood in the hallway.

Korczak leaned down as far as his painful back would

160

allow him. He brushed the boy's tousled locks. "What is it, son?"

"Help me?" the boy said.

Korczak led the boy to the toilet, raised his nightgown and positioned him. "Continue, Lieutenant," he said to Erwin.

While Korczak stood holding the boy, Erwin continued talking. "The question raised by the Jewish parents should be secondary to you. After all, a parent remains a parent. But you—you are important. You must go where you can best be employed; your work, your head, your life. You feel that you will die if you go East. That is why you are reluctant to cooperate in the resettlement program. But you will not die there. You have my word for it. You will be more useful not only to yourself but to the thousands of . . ."

Korczak again withdrew from the sound of Erwin's voice. He thought of World War I and an old blind Jew who stayed in Meszyniec and wandered perilously among wagons, horses, Cossacks, and artillery pieces. He remembered thinking at the time how cruel it had been to leave him behind. "They wanted to take him," Korczak was told. "But he refused to go because somebody had to look after the synagogue." Now, he was thinking, he was the old blind Jew.

After leading the sleepy child out of the W.C. and closing the door again, Korczak realized he must have said something to Erwin, protested in some way at something he had been saying, because Erwin had taken a new, conciliatory approach. It mattered little, however.

161

Korczak was too exhausted at this point to hear anything more than disjointed phrases.

Korczak returned to his seat. He made a halfhearted effort to straighten his back, then settled forward, resting his arms on his knees. He looked up at Erwin and suddenly envied him his youth and strength. "Ah," he thought, "if I could only have his body for a week. I would not use it to conquer worlds . . . only sleep."

". . . and it is true," Erwin was saying, "Jews have served mankind . . . talent . . . Moses . . . Christ . . . ancient race . . . Heine and Spinoza . . ."

It was a Czech news story Korczak was recalling. A ten-year-old maid in charge of a child wanted to sleep, so she strangled the baby. The poor girl had not seen any other solution.

". . . but there are other people besides Jews on the earth," Erwin leaned down and said directly at Korczak. "We Germans are not guilty. The problem existed long before. I grant it is hard for you. But it is not easy for us. Ours is a gigantic undertaking, and we must work methodically, according to plan."

Erwin stopped. In Korczak's mind the long jumble of speech was reduced to a single command: Volunteer to go to your death, and take your children with you.

"What will this problem look like in the future?" Korczak thought. He imagined an impressive stone building. Big rooms partitioned into small offices. Legal experts, doctors, philosophers, and advisers of differing ages and specialties. This is where one makes an application for death. Anyone is entitled to do so. But there are a few restrictions aimed at turning away frivolous applicants.

The authority cannot waste time. Special paper for the application, rules printed in Latin or Greek. Witnesses are present when it is handed in. Stamp duty, of course. A reason must be given: because of illness, valid; because of financial ruin, valid; because of ennui, valid; because a young German officer wants an old man and his orphans to die—*not valid!*

"No!" Korczak shouted. "Not valid! I will not take the children to their death!"

The sudden violence of Korczak's outburst shocked Erwin.

"What are you talking about?" Erwin asked. He now understood that although Korczak's eyes had been focused on him, he had not heard a word he had been saying. "I was telling you about the plan, how General Hahn has agreed that you and the children were not to have an armed guard . . . how the general has arranged for each child to receive bread and marmalade when they report for resettlement."

"Bread and marmalade indeed," Korczak said and started to laugh hysterically.

"You must be out of your mind," Erwin said. "I hope I do not have to explain the entire situation to you again."

"Nor do I, Herr Leutnant," Korczak muttered wearily. "I can appreciate that you have no stomach for this, that your superiors have arranged this meeting in the hope of luring me peacefully to my death."

"Herr Doktor," Erwin exclaimed, "I have already told you that you will not die! General Hahn has assured me personally that you will only be resettled. I have his word

163

for it. And you have my word—the word of a German officer and a gentleman."

Korczak noted how pale Erwin had gotten, how he was trembling.

"Believe me, Herr Doktor," Erwin went on. His voice was quiet now, and sincere. "I am offering you an opportunity to save yourself and your children. You are a Jew, you were kind to me once. And the children. Have you forgotten? I was an orphan too."

"Are you telling me that you have come here out of kindness, Lieutenant?" Korczak asked. "Out of sympathy?"

"No. I am here only in the performance of my duty. Had I been ordered to shoot you, I would have done so. But my orders are to help you resettle yourself and your children."

Korczak finally saw Erwin as he really was: a well-meaning innocent, the end product of a Nazi education. He was one of the enemy, an SS soldier, but he did not have murder in his heart. He pitied the boy for believing in what he himself felt was a treacherous lie. Or was there a chance, just a chance, that in this case Erwin had indeed arranged to save the children?

"Well, Herr Doktor?" Erwin asked.

Korczak hesitated. He wanted desperately to believe in miracles, but he could not. Erwin was the pawn sent through the ranks to checkmate the king. The only move now was to castle and fight for time.

"All right," Korczak said. "On the morning of August 7 we will be ready. That will give me time to prepare the

164

children, take care of my things, and get everything in order."

"Good," said Erwin with the air of one settling a friendly business arrangement. "Then it is agreed."

Erwin opened the W.C. door for the doctor and offered him his hand. Korczak looked at it, then shook his head. "Not yet," he said gently. "We will shake hands after August 7, when my children are resettled as you promise."

☆ 15 ☆

AFTER SCHNEIDER'S VISIT KORCZAK WAS LIKE A MAN IN Plato's cruel myth, "Gorgias," who constantly had before his eyes the date of his own death. The article in "Oif der Wach" confirmed what he knew in his heart to be true— the Jews were being systematically annihilated. "To report voluntarily to the Umschlagplatz for resettlement means to disappear for good," he wrote to his old friend Myron Zylberberg. "Take your wife and try to leave Warsaw. Perhaps just two of you can make it out."

Guards at the gates could be bribed, and some individuals had been able to escape the ghetto. Once outside, however, they were faced with the problem of survival in a community hostile to them. There was no way he could get two hundred children out of the ghetto, and even if the miracle could be arranged there was no place to take them.

The best he could do was try to save some of them, and he knew he had less than ten days to do it. He arranged for all the orphanage boys over the age of thirteen to be sent to a youth home at Gesia Street in the care of a teacher named Chojna. He felt the older boys could perhaps take care of themselves, while the little ones would be doomed to starve without his care. The thirteen-year-olds were deeply upset by this unexplained move. They felt rejected, and many wept bitterly as they filed away carrying their few belongings.

In mounting desperation Korczak investigated every possible avenue of escape or refuge for his children. On July 29 he attended a meeting of leaders of the Jewish community. A plan was being discussed to place several hundred Jewish children in monasteries in various parts of Poland. Until then, the Christian spiritual leaders had done little to save the Jews in their communities. But the assembled leaders were well aware that the Polish Catholic Church had often exploited the terrible moments in Jewish life as an excuse to convert adults and children. Now the Jewish elders were insistent that the children not be converted. "Some Jews must survive," they argued. Finally a plan was agreed upon: each Jewish child would pay six hundred zlotys for one year in advance. The cost of Jewish children unable to pay the fee would be covered by the children of the rich, who would be taxed double.

The plan only added to Korczak's pain and anxiety. He had just enough money to send two children, and he was concerned with each one of the 197 left in his care. He was faced with the same torture of decision which broke the spirit of thousands of Jewish parents. Who should be selected for extermination and who should live? The choice was so hideous, so degrading, that it further diminished the humanity of those who made it. To live under such circumstances was to choose to become less human.

In his diary, Korczak had considered just this problem. "When this war is over, many won't be able to look us in the eyes for fear of reading there the embarrassing questions, 'How is it that you are alive? How have you managed to survive?'"

July 30. Several members of the House Committee—the self-aid group of residents functioning in the area of the orphanage—came to Korczak with a scheme. They wanted to hide some of the children in the empty attics and basements of houses on streets already evacuated.

He considered the plan eagerly, hoping for the moment it was the miracle he sought, but in the end he opposed it, fearing the children would be hunted like wild animals and frightened to death a hundred times a day. He knew the Germans would comb the ghetto until they were found and publicly killed as an "example."

July 31. "Julek had his first peaceful night in weeks and I, too," Korczak wrote. In his bedroom isolation ward, Korczak now had young Julek instead of old Azrylewicz.

Julek had pneumonia, too. "The same groans, the same gestures, the same sufferings to tell about . . .

"The moment the day ceased impressing its dark and inimical visions, my dreams ceased. The law of equilibrium. A wearisome day, a relaxed night; a successful day, a feverish night. I could write a monograph about eiderdowns. Man and eiderdowns. Proletariat and eiderdowns.

"I am not ready to leave this world. Not for a long time. I tried to do so last night. In vain. I do not even know why I failed. Breath was weak. But the fingers were weak, too—no power flows through them.

"It was soft and warm in bed. It was hard to get up. But it is Saturday and on Saturday I weigh the children, before breakfast. For the first time I am not interested in the results. They must have put on weight. (I do not know why they gave them raw carrots for supper last night.)"

Mrs. Stefa helped with the weighing. The notations of weight loss or gain were dutifully made on each child's record.

That evening before going to sleep in a feverish, almost incoherent way, he noted in his diary how the face of the ghetto worsened every day. "1. Criminality. 2. Anesthesia. 3. Eccentricities. 4. Madhouses. 5. Gambling Hells. Monaco. The stake—one's head. The evidences of extermination multiply.

"The most important thing: everything has happened before. Wretched lives split between criminality and hospitals. Slavery: not only a strain of the muscles, but the honor and virginity of women. An ill-used family, motherhood, a discredited faith. Trading with spiritual goods.

"The children are in constant fear and uncertainty. 'A German will come and get you. He will catch you and put you in a sack.'

"Age is humiliation. Once it was good to grow old, now only health is of value. One buys strength and years of life nowadays. A scoundrel has a chance of achieving gray hairs."

To put himself to sleep he reread the Prophecies of Solomon. "I wonder whether Marcus Aurelius read the Prophecies?" he asked. "How soothing his diary is."

August 3. Korczak managed to get through the police cordon surrounding the police station where his assistant, Esther Winogron, was being held after her arrest the day before during a roundup for work details. "I was not certain whether I would be doing her a favor or not if I succeeded in getting her out," he wrote.

When a young Polish policeman politely asked how he had managed to get through the cordon, Korczak asked if something could be done to free Esther. The policeman said, "It is impossible," and warned him to be careful leaving the station.

"Thank you for the kind words," Korczak said.

The warning was well intended. In front of the police station a German soldier was having target practice with his Model 58 assault gun. He had bet his companions that he could kill a man at fifty yards with one burst, fired cowboy-style from the hip.

The other soldiers were calling out targets to the marksman, who, standing with his legs apart to brace the weapon, was shooting in rapid bursts. The street in front of the police station looked like a battlefield. Everyone had fallen flat on the cobbles, not daring to look up for fear they would be selected as targets. There was panic at an intersection fifty yards distant where the soldier was aiming. People were running, screaming, fighting to get out of the line of fire.

Korczak remained in the doorway of the police station, horrified, instinctively refraining from making any movement which might call attention to his presence. Then the sharpshooter turned his head. He caught sight of the group near the door, surveyed them casually with gun pointing toward Korczak, and shouted, "Come here, you. You there."

Korczak started slowly, fearfully, toward the soldier, but the man bellowed, "Not you. The priest." Korczak stepped back against the wall as a figure in a black cassock pushed past him. The priest walked slowly, head slightly bowed, hands clasped to his breast, lips moving in mute prayer.

"Show me your fat, Father," said the soldier.

The priest stood rigid.

"Your fat, Priest!" said the soldier, holding his hand out in an unmistakable gesture.

When the priest didn't move, one of the other soldiers stepped behind him and held his arms while the soldier in front tore open the cassock and yanked the priest's trousers open, ripping off the buttons. With the muzzle of his machine pistol he lifted the penis up and examined it. Satisfied that the priest had not been circumcised, he stepped back.

171

"You could have saved yourself a lot of trouble by showing me your fat when I asked for it," said the soldier, who then surveyed the crowd until he saw a bearded rabbi.

Pointing his gun at the rabbi he ordered him to come forward.

"Rabbi, ask the priest for a dance," said the soldier. "Quickly now. Don't be embarrassed. Pretend he is an elegant young shicksa. He's even wearing a skirt to make it easy for you."

The soldier prodded the rabbi with the muzzle of the gun. "Now, then, hurry and dance!" he commanded.

The two men grasped each other and slowly and awkwardly began a macabre dance. The Germans laughed, offered obscene suggestions, and continually yelled, "Faster, faster." Round and round they whirled, deathly pale, gasping for breath, until they fell exhausted to the street. The Germans, at last tired of their game, waved the crowd on about its business.

That night Korczak reflected on the events of day. With irony he wrote: "I do not accuse the Germans. They work, or rather they plan, logically and successfully. They are annoyed when they are disturbed. If one disturbs them, one is regarded as an idiot. I disturb, but they are thoughtful. They just take me and stand me against a wall. They are doing me a favor—for how easily a stray shot can hit me. And so I stand in safety against the wall. And I watch events and think."

As for Esther Winogron, he could only hope that if she did not return, "we shall meet her again somewhere else.

In the meantime we are convinced that she will continue to serve others, doing what is good and useful."

August 4. "I water the plants," he wrote in his diary. "Poor orphan plants. Plants of a Jewish orphanage. The dry earth greedily sucks up the water. A sentry watches me. Do I annoy him or amuse him at six o'clock in the morning? He stands and watches silently, his legs spread apart."

He received word that a ton of coal, promised him months earlier by a merchant, was ready for delivery. He ordered the coal sent to the orphanage at Dzielna Street, to Rose Abramowicz, for the time being. Someone asked him if the coal would be safe there. He answered with a smile.

That night was hot and moonless. It was after curfew, and only a few sounds drifted from the street up to Korczak's room—the tap-tapping of a prostitute's heels, the jingle and stamp of a passing patrol. Then he heard urgent rapping at the door. He glanced at his watch. It was 9:15 P.M. He went quickly to the door, opened it a crack, and peered out.

A young Jewish policeman he knew named Fels was leaning against the jamb, a cigarette in his mouth. His blue military cap with its Star of David was pushed to the back of his head, and he was swaying on his feet, obviously drunk. He had been pounding the door with his wooden truncheon.

When the door opened, the young policeman reached out to steady himself. "Excuse me, Doctor," he said. "But I came to tell you—tomorrow it's your turn to go for a train ride into the beautiful Polish countryside."

173

Korczak sagged back in horror. He thought he had an additional two days, and he had not ceased hoping for a miracle. Now the last shreds of hope had been torn from him. He was stripped naked, forced to face his doom.

The policeman smiled crookedly, trying somehow to ease the shock of his words. His eyes were red-rimmed and watery. "I'm drunk," he said, "but you'd be drunk too if you knew what I know."

Korczak stepped out onto the landing with the policeman and held his finger to his lips for quiet. "What do you know?" he whispered.

Tears began to stream from the boy's face. "I work in the ready room at Jewish Police Headquarters," he said. "What can the Germans do without our help? Without the Jewish Police? The Jewish Gestapo? Fine name for us, eh? I'm sure you call us that, too.

"But we aren't all bad. Some of us are human." The policeman reached into his hip pocket and pulled out a metal flask. He took a long pull, then wiped the mouth of the bottle and offered it to Korczak, who impatiently shook his head.

"Did you have something you wanted to tell me?" he asked.

"I work at the ready room," the boy said again. "Every day the orders for the next day's deportation is posted there. Last night my own block was listed. I told my mother to hide with friends. This morning when we rounded up the block do you know who was in the group?"

The policeman grasped Korczak's arm, pleading with him to understand. "My mother was there. What was I

174

to do? One word of protest from me and they would have put a bullet into my head. What was I to do? If it would have helped her I would have said something, done something. But all I could have done was get us both shot.

"She understood. She whispered to me not to say anything. So I herded her into the Umschlagplatz with the others. I saw her train leave." The boy's body rocked with sobbing. "No one comes back from the East, doctor," he cried. "No one."

He looked into Korczak's eyes. "Tomorrow it's your turn," he said. "This whole block is to be evacuated. I saw it on the board tonight."

The boy looked at Korczak beseechingly. "You must do something," he said.

"What can I do?" Korczak asked quietly.

"I don't know," the boy cried. "Something."

Korczak shut the door gently against the boy's retreating footsteps and went back into the house to look for Stefa. He found her in the girl's dormitory and beckoned.

Outside in the corridor he told her quietly, "Tomorrow is the day for deportation. I just learned it from a Jewish policeman."

Stefa accepted the news without comment. Her calmness disturbed Korczak. "You know what that means?" he said. "Deportation means death."

"That's not true," said Stefa.

"Have you read what Friedrych wrote in 'Oif der Wach'?" he asked.

"I've read it," Stefa said. "But the Socialists are only trying to stir the Jews up to fight."

He looked at her, stunned. Then it dawned on him.

175

She had known the truth from the beginning. She knew it when she returned to Warsaw from her safe refuge in Palestine. He saw that many had known in their hearts what was happening, but they preferred to ignore it. This refusal to accept the terrible facts was what kept the weak from despair. He did not have the right to take the crutch of illusion away from her.

So the final decision for all of us is mine, he realized. I must make it alone. He looked toward the ceiling of the room and murmured a heartfelt question: "Oh, God, what is Thy will?" Even as he did he smiled wryly, thinking how pious one becomes in time of need.

Stefa saw the smile and misunderstood it. "You were not serious then," she said. "You didn't mean what you said. You were only playing a terrible game with me."

"I was playing a terrible game," he said, knowing now that the game must be played to the end.

He walked into the dormitory and waved his hand for silence. The children looked at him eagerly. "A fairy tale?" Hancia asked.

"No, not a fairy tale tonight," he said, seating himself on Hancia's bed.

He sent Rosia to get the boys from their dormitory, and when all the children were assembled he stood up.

"I have an announcement. Tomorrow we are all going to the country, to Goclawek, for a holiday. Tonight you must all sleep well, so you will be fresh in the morning. Good night, dear ones."

As always, when he was sorely troubled, he went to his desk. A letter from Myron Zylberberg required an answer. One of their friends, a man named Fernster who had

176

been baptized a Christian, had died. His wife wanted him buried outside of the ghetto in a Christian cemetery. His friends believed he should be interred in the Jewish cemetery.

"In spite of the fact that he was baptized a Christian he suffered as a Jew and died as one," Korczak wrote.

That was the truth of it in his mind, the way it was for all Jews, even those who considered themselves Poles or Germans or Americans. In the eyes of the world they would be counted as Jews. In the end, they would die as Jews.

"To be a Jew is to accept—and endure," he wrote in his diary.

He had endured for a long time, almost too long, but it was only recently that he had begun to accept the fact that he was a Jew first, a Pole second. And his mind went back to his childhood, and his father.

✡

✡   BOOK TWO   ✡

✡

BOOK TWO

1

Josef Goldszmidt, Korczak's father, was an intellectual liberal, typical of many Polish Jews at the turn of the
century who believed that assimilation was merely a
question of goodwill. He considered himself a Pole first,
a Jew second. He spoke only Polish, educated his children
in Polish schools and brought them up in a bourgeois
Polish environment.

Josef wanted his children to think of themselves as
international citizens, and he acknowledged his religious
background only when filling in the appropriate spaces

on official application forms. He had no allegiance to any religious institution, and he didn't encourage his children to have any.

Like many Jewish Poles, Josef admired Germany and its culture. Among the books on the shelves which covered three walls of his library was a collection of German poets: Klopstock, Goethe, Schiller, and Heine in gold-stamped bindings, as well as the works of Leibnitz, Kant, Hegel. He and most of his friends privately considered that the Poles as a group were barbarians, the Germans a truly cultured nation.

Josef was bald before he was thirty and in the Gentile fashion of the times sported a full moustache. When he went to his office he wore a flowing cloak, a broad-brimmed plush hat, and a wide cravat. Starched white cuffs protruded from his sleeves and diamonds twinkled in his cuff links. On his waiscoat a gold chain bobbed up and down. When he went out he carried a walking stick with a stag handle ornamented with silver.

He was encouraged in his assimilation by his wife, who was also from a Polonized family. Cecylia Gebicka was a cultured woman. She was small and dark, with attractive long black hair which she faithfully brushed one hundred times each night before going to bed.

Henryk, as Korczak was named, was born July 21, 1879, although his birth was not recorded in the Office of the Registrar of Warsaw until some years later. Josef was probably being cautious, not negligent. Parents often postponed registering the birth of their sons in Russian-occupied Poland to give the young man a better chance to escape conscription in the Russian Army.

182

Henryk was named after his grandfather in violation of the Jewish tradition of naming a child for a living relative. But it was the grandfather who had begun the family's assimilation process. A doctor, no small achievement in the nineteenth century for a Jew whose father had been a glazier, he gave all his children Christian names: Maria, Louis, Magdalena, Jacob, Carol, and Josef. And Josef in turn gave his children Christian names: Henryk and Anna.

Josef loved comfort and the Goldszmidts lived in the affluence befitting his income and status in the community. Their home was in Nowy Swiat, an elegant residential section of Warsaw called The New World. The entrance to Choldana 140 was through a front door with frosted glass panels. Then a flight of marble steps. On a mahogany double door on the third floor was a brass plate with his father's name engraved on it. When the bell was pressed a maid in a spotless white apron and starched white hat would answer the door and accept the visitor's card, which would be placed on a silver tray and brought to one of the elders.

The high-ceilinged apartment was richly decorated with glowing Oriental rugs, velvet drapes, heavy carved furniture, marble-topped tables, little boxes of lapis lazuli and tortoise shell, with vases and busts and dark oil paintings on the wall.

The dining room was dominated by an oversized table usually covered by an embroidered white linen tablecloth. Eight heavy oak chairs with high backs upholstered in velvet surrounded the table. A credenza against one wall was burdened with wine decanters, a samovar, trays, and

183

vases. Behind the glass panes were crystal glasses, china, and polished silver dishes. A heavy oil lamp that could be raised or lowered on bronze chains hung from the ceiling.

When company came, every lamp was lighted and the apartment glowed and sparkled. The entry hall was full of fur-lined coats, tall silk hats, and fashionable millinery. Mrs. Goldszmidt, in a graceful long dress, her hair elaborately piled on her head, greeted guests at the door and led them into the salon.

The salon itself was a spacious room with four long windows and a carved ceiling with traces of gold paint. Around the walls stood wide easy chairs upholstered in burgundy satin, brocaded sofas, and heavy mahogany credenzas. A chandelier hung from the ceiling, its gilt candlesticks and crystal prisms softly lighting the room. Against one wall was a grand piano, a hallmark of affluence and culture.

Henryk studied at that piano for three hours a week and hated it. As a child, he was introspective and imaginative. His happiest hours were spent reading books like the tales of Hans Christian Andersen and the Brothers Grimm, to the despair of his parents who said he would ruin his eyes. When his parents put out the lamp in his bedroom, he would get up at dawn to finish a story.

He first became aware that he was a Jew, therefore different, soon after his eighth birthday. One Saturday morning he found his canary dead in its cage. He carefully opened the cage door. With his favorite pen (it had a little glass window at one end through which he could see a colored view of the Alps) he prodded the canary gently from the other side of the cage toward the door.

He was afraid to touch the bird with his hands. He did not know what disease one got from touching death but he was certain it was bad. He had to bend the legs toward the body to get it through the door and into a can which had once contained sour lemon drops.

Then he closed the lid and put the covered tin on his dresser. He glanced at it from time to time with tear-filled eyes as he took off his long nightgown and dressed in his Saturday play clothes: leather shorts, a sweater, and sandals.

Coffin in hand, he went to the kitchen, his favorite place in the house. Like most kitchens of the time, it was built around an enormous tiled stove. Copper pots and pans hung from hooks on the walls, and the smell of freshly baked cakes and cinnamon made his mouth water.

Ludwicka, the maid, and Maria, the cook, were busy preparing the midday meal of latkes—pancakes made of grated potatoes, fried in olive oil, and sprinkled with sugar and butter. The stove spread its heat throughout the room and the sunlight shining in through the window curtains was reflected in the oven tiles.

His breakfast was waiting for him on the big oak table: rolls, butter, and coffee, which was mostly chicory. Judging by the dishes in the sink, his older sister, Anna, had already eaten. His parents had not awakened yet because the tray with their breakfast was on the sideboard.

Maria noticed the tin of lemon drops and clucked disapprovingly. "You will ruin your appetite with sweets so early in the morning," she said.

"I finished them long ago," he said, holding the tin tightly.

"Then what do you have in it?" said Ludwicka.

"I'll show you, but you won't like it," he said.

"Show me," challenged Ludwicka.

He pushed his chair back and went to Ludwicka. When he removed the cover, Ludwicka shrieked.

"I told you you wouldn't like it," he said.

"What are you going to do with it?" she asked.

"I'm going to make a cross and bury it in the court-yard," he said, tears starting to well up in his eyes.

"You can't do that," said Ludwicka. "The canary doesn't have a Christian soul like a human being. And weeping for it is a sin."

Later, in the courtyard, he felt even worse when Smyrna, the caretaker's son, said the canary was Jewish "because you are a Jew. I am a Catholic, and when I die I will go to heaven. Jews go to hell."

He asked if it would be dark there, because he was afraid of the dark; he was even afraid to enter a dark room. Smyrna assured him it would be dark as pitch.

Later that morning he knocked timidly on the door of his father's study. Josef Goldszmidt was a highly respected barrister in Warsaw, an author, and a recognized authority on divorce law. To his son he was a fount of information on all subjects.

Asked if it was true that there was a special Catholic heaven different from that of the Jews, Josef answered firmly: "This is childish nonsense. All people are alike. They all go to the same heaven."

"But Smyrna said I might go to hell where it is dark, and I am afraid," protested Henryk.

"I tell you it is not so," said his father, an edge of anger to his voice. "We are all alike—Poles, Jews, Germans, Catholics. We are all one people."

"But, Smyrna said . . ." protested Henyrk.

"Smyrna was wrong," interrupted Josef. "I tell you we are all one people."

When he was eight, Henryk discovered that the Christian children in school had prayers, so he made up his own, which he said every night before he went to sleep: "Sir, I am coming to you as a lone man. I beg you to give me this thing that a man needs, the talent to pray with all his heart. Let disappear from my eyes and heart all things I don't want to think about and which will distract me from my prayer. Teach me how to pray to you with all my heart and belief."

Often he would stand for hours in front of his bedroom window wistfully watching the activity in the courtyard below, wishing he could take part in it, but his parents forbade it.

"My parents told me that poor children were dirty, used bad language, their hair was crawling with lice, they were sick and I might catch some disease from them," he wrote later. "They told me that poor children threw stones, fought and poked children in the eyes. I was forbidden to go and play in the courtyard for fear of such things.

"Life taught me otherwise. Poor children weren't sick. They played and ran around all day, drank fresh water from the well which my parents said might have been contaminated; poor kids bought cheap but tasty sweets and their ugly language was funny.

"My mother said I had no ambition. She said it was of no consequence to me how I dressed or with whom I

187

played. Whether they were the children of my own class or the concierge was all the same to me. They were small like myself. That was good enough for me. Besides, I was only a few years old and couldn't solve the problems of the poor, hungry, and dirty children of our courtyard.

"It was not without justification that my father called me, as a child, a donkey or fathead and, in moments of anger, an idiot. Only my dear grandmother believed in my star. She gave me raisins to eat and called me her philosopher."

Although he became friends with the son of the caretaker, Henryk's mother discouraged the children from playing together. She instructed the maids to tell Smyrna if he came to the door that Henryk was not at home. Once he caught Ludwicka in the act of telling such a lie. His mother explained: "Smyrna is from the street, and you might learn some bad things from him."

Henryk was always under the watchful eyes of his parents, grandmother, and the maids. The word "No" was one he heard most often. Most objects were covered with dangerous germs. He was told never to talk to strangers. As a result, his childish imagination was filled with frightening fantasies. Once while shopping on the street with his mother she gave him two coins to toss to a beggar. "Give them to him so he won't do anything to you," she said. "Otherwise he might come and put you in a sack and throw you into the Vistula."

For nights afterward he dreamed that the beggar would get him. It was only in later life, when he had to beg for himself and his orphans, that he could comment with irony on his mother's words.

188

There were, of course, happier memories. He recalled "the lovely thrills and spontaneity with which my sister and I greeted even the most excessive pursuits of pleasure which our father provided with uncanny intuition and inventiveness.

"He mercilessly pulled our ears and twisted them. He bought ice cream and soda drinks in winter but when as a result we fell ill he hardly left our bedsides and cooled our foreheads with a loving hand. Mother was nervous and forbidding on such occasions. She eased him out of the nursery, but Father was magnificent, magnanimous, incalculable, and loving."

His favorite memories were of time spent alone with his father. Holding tightly to his father's hand he was led through the busy streets of Warsaw. They would go to the market in Grzybowsky Place where the air smelled of lemons, apples, pears, Hungarian plums, black and white grapes, and watermelons. Street peddlers called out their wares and the women hucksters haggled noisily with customers who pinched, prodded, and lifted the glowing fruit to make sure they got the best.

When it was dark, the stalls were lit with lanterns or flickering dangles. Frequently they went home by droshky, the horse and carriage clip-clopping through the streets, the boy cuddled for warmth under his father's great coat. When they reached home his father would take a silver coin out of a deep chamois purse. Then, cradling the drowsy boy in his arms, he would carry him upstairs and lay him tenderly on his bed.

On Sundays Henryk and Anna often went for walks with the maid, Ludwicka. They would promenade through the Square of Alexander the Holy to the Church of the Three Crosses where Ludwicka would attend mass. As the children entered the cold quiet of the church, they always worried that because they were not Catholic something terrible would happen to them. They would follow Ludwicka's lead in making the sign of the cross and stand beneath the Holy Mother on a stained glass window while Ludwicka prayed.

After Mass they would go into the street and buy cakes and candy from a peddler in the Iron Gate Square. While Ludwicka had a rendezvous with a beau in front of the big Russian church the children could run and play.

The rendezvous was one secret between themselves and Ludwicka. The other was the fact that they had a Christmas tree. Ludwicka used to smuggle a small one into the kitchen for Henryk and Anna to admire. Henryk longed to boast to Smyrna that he too had a Christmas tree, but he never revealed the secret.

When he was seven, Henryk started to attend the Szmurly School on Freta Street. "In general, schools in my day were not much good. They were dreadfully severe. Nothing was allowed. The atmosphere of the school building was cold and I dreamed of it in my sleep and invariably woke up in a cold sweat. I was always happy to find it was not a real experience but only a dream."

Physical punishment was liberally dispensed. Undoubtedly his active opposition to corporal punishment for children stemmed from his own experiences.

Of those days he wrote: "Whenever it was easy to get hurt, to end up with a black eye for defending a cause or some principle of justice, I somehow managed to be there. Trouble and I were magnetized in favor of each other."

He earned good grades, however, probably because students were called on to answer questions in alphabetical order. Since his last name began with a G, there was rarely a day when he did not have to recite. He became proficient in German as well as Russian; the tongue of the oppressor was forced on all secondary-school children. And even in the third form he was concerned about educational reform. In a school paper he wrote solemnly: "To reform the world around us means that the system of education must undergo radical changes."

School had only one saving grace: he could wear long uniform pants instead of short trousers. He recalled many years later that he had to go for his high-school test in the same month that his long hair was cut short.

Although shy, he had a score of love affairs, starting from the age of seven. "Curiously enough, I remember many of them," he wrote when he was sixty-three. "There were two sisters from the ice rink in Warsaw, my cousin Stalie (her grandfather was Italian and she was in mourning). Then Sophia Kalhorn, Anielka, Irena from Laneczow, Stefa for whom I stole flowers from the lawns near the fountain of the Saxon Gardens. I loved for a week, a month, sometimes two or three months. Some girls I would like to have for sisters, others for a wife, or wife's sister."

And always, in spare moments, he wrote—short stories, songs, and poems. His mother once discovered in his desk a sheet on which he had written a poem. When she told

Josef he stormed at his son, shouting that writers were poor and led miserable lives. "Be sensible—study medicine and be a respected doctor like your grandfather," he ordered.

Unfortunately, Josef did not live to see his son become a doctor. When Henryk was ten his father suffered a nervous breakdown. The usual treatment for mentally disturbed people was incarceration in an insane asylum which was more of a prison than a hospital. Josef, a troubled ghost of his former self, was released for a while, then returned to the asylum and died there when Henryk was eleven.

Despite his lack of religious belief, Josef had been an important man in the Jewish community and services were held for him in Warsaw's biggest synagogue. It was the first time that Henryk had been in a synagogue and despite his grief he was awed and fascinated by the pageantry around him. He was proud that so many people were attending his father's funeral and wished Smyrna could have seen the homage done him. From time to time he craned his head to look for his mother and sister, black-veiled and surrounded by a group of wailing women in the balcony.

The candles were lit and the rabbi said the services in rapid Hebrew with a chorus of responses from the congregation. Then his grandfather in white tallith with black stripes, looking like a king from an eastern country, recited the Kaddish, the prayer for the dead, in front of the Torah. Henryk for the first time saw his grandfather as a Jew.

Although he understood none of the Hebrew, Henryk

became aware for the first time that he shared a common bond with the Jews in the synagogue. He recalled some of the words the rabbi had said at his father's grave the day before: "The Jew more than any other man realizes himself within his national community. As a Jew he can exist only insofar as he belongs to it."

The words meant little to Henyrk then, though they were to prove prophetic fifty years later.

2

THE DEATH OF HIS FATHER HAD A TRAUMATIC EFFECT ON young Henryk. There is evidence throughout all of his later life and writings that he feared that he too had inherited insanity. As a result of this conviction he never considered marriage, certain that he had the taint of madness in his blood which would be passed on to his children.

Henryk had grown up isolated from the world of Jewry by his wealth and his father's beliefs. Suddenly he and his mother and sister were moved out of their big

194

apartment into cramped quarters in the Warsaw slums. The ancestors of most of the Jews there had come from Germany in the fourteenth century when, in more than 350 parishes, Jews were drowned, burned, broken on the wheel, strangled, buried alive. The survivors escaped into Poland where they were forced to live precariously at the mercy of every official caprice, subject to instant change when a new set of conquerors occupied the city. Poland's Jews were second-class citizens with few legal rights and little status in the community—a far cry from Josef's teachings of one world for all men.

In the tradition of the times Henryk became the man of the family. Young though he was, it was expected he would take over support of the family. Soon he was earning money after school by coaching slow students. Eventually he had so many pupils that he had to walk or run from lesson to lesson; only rarely could he afford the few groschen needed to ride on one of the red-painted tram cars which clanged by.

As an overly protected child Henryk had always found it difficult to establish relationships with children his own age. As a breadwinner he put even further distance between himself and his contemporaries. He had no time for the sports or games which interested most teen-agers so he took to spending his free time either with younger children who made no demands of him but accepted him as one of them or with old people.

He liked to visit the Saxon Gardens in the heart of Warsaw where, in the beautiful green park by the fountains where stone sea dragons sprayed water from their mouths, he found old people to talk with who admired him and called him "the little philosopher."

In his diary, he noted that he dreamed about "a station in life as a doctor in a small town. And I thought about love. One summer in Warsaw when I was fourteen love grew to a mania that disturbed my spirit."

The girl was one of his pupils, the daughter of a wealthy Jewish merchant. They would sometimes meet in the Saxon Gardens. She wore a green, caracul-bordered jacket with a broad-brimmed hat, and she was the most beautiful girl he had seen. When he could afford it they would go to the coffeehouse at the south edge of the park and share a chocolate under the varicolored panes of glass.

That same year, as often happens with adolescents, Henryk was also stirred by his first strong religious feelings. He never explained his concept of God then, but his notes indicate that the Creator had become more personal and was no longer the "Sir" to whom he addressed his childhood prayers. But he was still a long way from embracing the traditional concept of either a Jewish or a Christian God.

His taste in reading matured. He devoured the works of great Polish writers like Adam Mickiewicz, Stefan Zeromski, and the favored Russian writer of the time, Leo Tolstoi. In his boyish enthusiasm he often wrote to established authors like Belmont, whom he told: "What a masterpiece you have created!" He wrote Jesk-Choinski, "You are great! Your 'Dying Sparks' is a magnificent work. How you have mastered the human soul."

He continued to write poetry, and recorded a daydream in which he imagined the reaction of a publisher to one

196

of his poems. The letter of rejection would read: "The answer to your inquiry, sir—it won't be published." And once, reality matched fantasy.

Taking along some of his poems, he visited a famous Polish editor of a Sunday newspaper. He later confided to a friend, "I recited to him with trembling voice one of my first poems. Alexander Swietochowski listened attentively while I declaimed:

" 'Ah! Let me die!

" 'Ah! Don't let me live!

" 'Ah! Let me descend to my dark grave!'

"To which Swietochowski retorted, 'I'll let you.' "

Henryk never again tried to write poetry, but his black mood persisted. At seventeen he started to write a novel entitled *Suicide*. The hero, like himself, began to hate life because he was in constant fear of going mad—Henryk was still strongly influenced by the death of his father. The novel was rejected for publication at precisely the time Henryk had to decide what he was going to do with the rest of his life: become a writer or a doctor.

"I will not be a writer," he told a school friend. "What else is there left for me? To be a quack? Perhaps so. After all, literature is only words, whereas medicine is deeds. I must earn a regular living. A literary career is too unsteady, journalism too risky, and the teaching profession is out of the question because of the oppressive measures imposed by the Russians."

Although he rarely had time to do his own homework, his brilliant oral answers offset the poor marks he obtained for hastily written work and he was an honors student. There was a small Jewish quota at Warsaw University and he was accepted as a medical student on scholarship, because of his marks and his grandfather's prestige.

At the University, Henryk sported a small ginger-colored beard and wore the student cap: blue with a red band. His grades were good and he survived the usual hazing medical students got from their professors. His anatomy professor, he remembered years later, once stabbed at the inside of his left palm with his right index finger and said to Henryk, "Hair will grow here sooner than you will become a doctor."

Although a full-time student he still continued as a tutor to earn his living. Nevertheless he felt the need to continue writing: he wrote papers about social problems, poverty and inequality of wealth. And his reading habits changed. Slavic writers no longer satisfied him, and he read extensively in the works of Dante, Shakespeare, and Schiller. He carried books in his pockets to read between classes or when lectures were dull.

When he was eighteen and a second-year medical student, Henryk decided to enter a competition for writers under the sponsorship of Paderewski. He sent in a drama entitled "Which Way?" Searching for a suitable and impressive *nom de plume* that would appeal to the panel of judges he came upon a book by Kraszewski, a well-known nineteenth-century Polish writer, entitled *About Janasz Korczak*. He scribbled the name on his manuscript and had it published himself. The compositor who set the title page of the book accidentally changed the name to Janusz Korczak.

Because of his busy schedule, Henryk had time for very few friends. The one who was closest to him was L. S.

Licinski, author of *Hallucinations* and *A Hobo's Memoirs*, books which gave a vivid picture of the troubled mood of Polish youth in the early years of the twentieth century. The country had just lived through a series of uprisings, all of them abortive. Poland was divided, crushed, and rebellious. The youth of the country had lost faith in their strength. They resorted to fantasy to relieve their frustration and in fact attempted to commit spiritual suicide. Many of that generation became heavy drinkers.

Licinski was on the verge of madness and was dying of tuberculosis. His problems fascinated Henryk. A faded photograph of Licinski shows him as tall and thin, with a long pale face, a high, prematurely furrowed forehead, keen eyes, thin lips, and a sharp chin covered with a sprouting beard. His hair was combed back from his ears and he sported a long scarf wrapped around his throat. Licinski led a completely Bohemian life. His haunts were whore houses, bistros where knife fights were frequent, and taverns in the ancient section of Warsaw.

Henryk's mother protested the friendship. In a protest of his own soon after he was nineteen, Henryk left the family flat and moved into a hovel in Warsaw's poorest quarter, romantically determined to observe depravity "at its worst and grandest."

He wanted to do more than just observe, however. He intended to experience the extreme poverty of these people as both a doctor and a writer. For the first time he was beginning to feel that perhaps he could combine both careers!

With Licinski as guide, he discovered the incredible squalor of a droshky driver's lodgings in Solec, a poverty-ridden suburb on the banks of the Vistula. In one room lived nearly a dozen illiterate children to whom Henryk attempted to teach the rudiments of grammar.

He spent time in Powisle near the River Wishile. Inhabited by sewage and garbage workers, beggars sang in its alleys in quavering voices, cripples stretched out stumps of arms, and thousands of homeless urchins lived on their own without any adult care or interest.

The objective observations he made as a medical student strengthened his reactions as a writer. "I want to write of human minds, of miseries, and of happiness, of fights with evil, of brotherhood, of love—in short, of the Morrow of Humanity," he told Licinski. And as a result of living among the poor of Warsaw, Henryk decided to choose pediatrics as his medical specialty.

In 1900, when Henryk was twenty-one, he was required to take his military service, but as a medical student had to serve only two years. When he returned to Warsaw University he was one of a "limited but distinguished" company chosen by Alexander Pajewski, the editor of a satirical weekly called *Thorns*, to write part of a serialized novel entitled "Memoirs of a Crazy Butler." The work was to be unique because it would be written by half a dozen promising young talents.

Kazimierz Pollack, who was one of the group, recalls that all the other contributors wrote one part except Henryk, who was responsible for three under the pen name of HEN–RYK.

Pajewski was so impressed with Henryk's talent that he asked him to become a regular contributor to *Thorns*. He also sponsored publication of Henryk's first novel,

The Waifs, written under the pseudonym of Janusz Korczak. In the dedication of the novel Henryk wrote: "It walks along a narrow path. Longing for and clutching the leading hand of parents and school, a waif is pushed along the wide road of life and nothing protects his eyes, his ears, his mind from absorbing what a wide, crowded highway can stuff into them."

The success of his first novel prompted Henryk to write another book, *Nonsense*, satirical short stories dealing with problems of the day. *Nonsense* was also a success.

Meanwhile, he earned his medical diploma at Warsaw University and decided to take his clinical work abroad, focusing on pediatrics.

"I supplemented my doctorate in medicine with clinical studies in Berlin, Paris, and London, where I learned the benefits of charitable institutions in a nation's life—what a profitable experience. All my free time I spent visiting orphanages, corrective and penal institutions for children. I spent one month in a home for retarded children and one month in the neurological clinic in Ziehen."

As a young doctor abroad Henryk was always short of money. Frequently two glasses of milk and a slice of bread made up the whole of his daily diet, but any hardships were trivial in comparison to the knowledge he was acquiring.

"Berlin hospitals and German medical literature taught me to think of what I already knew and how to move forward in that field," he wrote. "Slowly and systematically Paris taught me to think of what we still do not know but desire, must and will learn. Berlin's was a full day of small, detailed troubles and their answers. Paris's

201

was a vision of tomorrow with the exalted, urgent feeling of hope and unexpected triumph. The seriousness of want, the anxiety of ignorance, and the thrill of research—that was Paris. And the great synthesis of the child—that was my dream when I sat in the Parisian Library of Medicine and read with flushed cheeks the thick volumes of French classical clinicists."

When Henryk returned to Warsaw in 1903 he was distressed to find that although he had changed, Warsaw was the same. He was full of enlightened opinions and advanced medical knowledge, but no one in Warsaw seemed impressed. More important, medical colleagues did not even care to hear what he had to say.

After months of unsuccessful job hunting he was so depressed that he suggested to Anna, his sister, that they commit suicide: he because he lacked a place in the world and she because of an unhappy love affair. They took no action, however, because they could not come to an agreement on either the method or the reasons. As they argued, both came to realize that life was not so bad after all and they were too young to give up so quickly.

A few weeks later Henryk got his first post, as a doctor in the Children's Hospital in Sliska Street and discovered he was in demand almost as much because of his literary reputation as for his skill in pediatrics. His "Humoresques" in *Thorns* and his articles in *The Voice*, the Polish Socialist Party weekly, plus his first books, *The Waifs* and *Nonsense*, put him in favor among the intelligentsia, and the rich bourgeois wanted to meet the man who so scathingly and humorously ridiculed them.

In one story he sketched a profile of a landlord who

wished to marry his daughter to someone who was wealthy and in this way secure the funds to send his son to the university. So the landlord raised the rents in his apartment block, setting off a chain of tragic and unforeseen incidents.

In another story entitled "Do-Gooders" he wrote sarcastically of the long list of donations by the rich published in daily newspapers. He reminded his readers that the newspaper offered accounts of "floods, fires, tragedy, tuberculosis, news of student's pranks, of actresses, all mixed up with two tears and a rouble." He denounced sarcastically the ulterior motives which prompted legacies to charities for the purpose of denying the money to some expectant beneficiary. He compared the large sums spent by the rich on clothing, cigars, imported wines, and gambling with the miserable amounts of "grosz" set aside for the poor. He also complained of the ostentatious way charitable contributions were made: well-dressed children of the rich whose parents gave them a kopeck to press into the hand of a crippled beggar in front of the church on Sunday morning, where there were plenty to witness "the act of charity."

He was still torn between medicine and writing. Medicine was his career and writing was an outlet for his creativity and social conscience. At times he went to his sister Anna's flat at Zlota 8 to read books and write. There, upstairs in the attic, he began to write a somewhat fictionalized autobiography entitled *A Child of Society*.

He was well into the book when once again he was mobilized into the Prussian Imperial Army as a captain in the Medical Corps. It was 1904 and the Russo-Japanese campaign was in full swing. Doctors were needed in the Far East, and Korczak was sent to the advanced base hospital at Harbin, Manchuria, in a train filled with soldiers and their gear. The sawdust-strewn floor was filthy, and the car stank of cheap tobacco. A Polish soldier jeered, "You are the only Jew I've seen on this train and naturally, you are a doctor. Jews are not fighters. They hide under their rabbi's skirts."

A recruit who heard the insult rose and without a word knocked the man down. "I'm a Jew," he said, "and this man may one day save your worthless life."

Korczak was eventually attached to the hospital train which traveled in Siberia between Harbin and Chava-rowsk. He also wrote articles as the war correspondent for *The Voice*. In one report he wrote of his journey on a hospital train full of wounded soldiers. "There was no means of communication between the coaches—there were no connecting doors—and I had to use station stops or halts to transfer from one coach to another. Having finished dressing a soldier's wounds and giving medicines I would seat myself on the edge of a bunk and recite Krilow's poetry to the men."

He dressed wounds, amputated limbs, and functioned efficiently as a doctor under primitive, sometimes almost impossible, circumstances. But as always he was concerned with the plight of children. He noted with anger that the canes used by Chinese schoolmasters to punish students were too thick.

Meanwhile, in Poland, the people were rebelling against the injustice, oppression, and corruption under Russian domination. The Russian authorities kept even the most talented Poles from expressing themselves as useful members of the community. Scientists equipped to fill university chairs were reduced to giving private tutoring. Inventive geniuses wasted their talents trying to improve corsets. Swietochowski, one of the country's great journalists, wrote of talented Poles: "They are like diamonds deserving to glitter in a royal tiara. Instead they are used to cut glass for stable windows."

The Socialists led the revolution of 1905, and the fact that it was crushed had an effect on the people, especially the Jews. Hassidic youth cast off their gaberdines, shaved their faces, became strikers and Zionists. Daughters of respectable Jewish homes fell in love with university students and ran off with them to New York or Palestine. Mothers discarded their traditional matron's wigs and let the world see their own hair. Speakers contended that Jews should not wait for the Messiah to come but should build the Jewish homeland with their own hands. Boys and girls secretly met in cellars and attics and conspired against the Czar.

Such activities drew a violent reaction from the ruling groups: the Jews were persecuted more and more. The National Democrats began to dominate politics by feeding the middle class on religious and patriotic slogans. They preached anti-Semitism, in an attempt to focus attention on the Jews rather than on the real enemy, the Russians.

When he returned to Warsaw, Korczak found the city torn by outbreaks of street fighting between Polish Socialists and Russian soldiers. He was mobilized again. Although wearing the uniform of a Russian Army officer, he did not hesitate to dress the wounds of workers hurt in the bitter struggle. He sympathized with the Socialist Party and wrote articles for *The Voice*, defending the workers' right to holidays, a radical position then. He advocated insurance against illness, championed women's rights, a just distribution of the land, medical assistance, funeral insurance, cooperative movements, agrarian and educational reform. He was even bold enough to claim that workers had the right to strike. In one article he said: "Maybe a miracle will happen and a knight of a hundred heads and a hundred steely arms will arrive and buy for all of us and our children a better tomorrow. History dreams a strange dream."

Such articles did not endear Korczak to the Establishment. He was accused of propagating radical and Masonic ideologies and sentenced to six months' imprisonment in the Tenth Pavilion of the Warsaw Citadel. His cellmates included Comrade Bernard, the most famous Socialist leader in Warsaw, and Professor Krzwycki, a well-known scientist.

The three men found much to talk about during the long days and nights of their imprisonment. Years later, when Korczak was jailed by the Germans, he said it was his old cellmates' example he tried to imitate when suffering the frustrations and injustices of confinement.

While in jail Korczak completed *A Child of Society*, in which he described sardonically the decadence and hopelessness of the man who has been derailed from his true course in life. The book made him a social lion again, and when he returned to his job as an intern at the Bereson Hospital, he found it difficult to tell whether parents

206

called him to attend their children or because they wanted to say they had had *the* Dr. Korczak at their homes.

Although he continued to write articles with a socialist leaning, he gradually turned away from politics as a means of achieving desirable ends. He made no more ideological speeches and dissociated himself from all political declarations. He confined himself solely to children's problems. He criticized bourgeois methods of upbringing and condemned social snobbery and its influence on the child. He was equally scathing in his treatment of prejudice and superstitious social customs. He began his battle for the rights and privileges of the child with the same enthusiasm that he had given to social and medical reforms.

He put the emancipation of children on an equal footing with the liberation of the peasant, the worker, Jews, and women, stating that the rights of the child were as important as the rights of adults. In his writing he pleaded for equal rights for children. "Isn't it the greatest happiness for a man to live, to work, and to fight for a better tomorrow? And the child is our tomorrow. Just like the political parties: as they consolidate their power, they change the sandcastles into the bread of real achievement."

In 1907 Henryk volunteered to organize a summer camp for underprivileged children under the auspices of the Warsaw Welfare Society. He took Jewish boys from Pawia and Nalweki Streets and Christian boys from other slum areas in the city to Michalowek for three weeks of vacation.

At camp he discovered a tender bond between nature

and the children, most of whom had never before been in the country. He played with the children in the fields and woods, helped them hunt flowers to decorate their tents, taught them which mushrooms were edible and worth picking for supper.

Shy himself, young and clumsy, he did not play games skillfully, so he did not compete with them on an adult level and make them feel inferior. A photograph taken at the time shows him on the steps of a wooden bungalow surrounded by skinny, barefoot, shaven-headed boys, brown-skinned after weeks in the sun. The boys wore lederhosen and he was wearing trousers, an open-necked shirt with sleeves rolled up, and sandals.

At night he told lovely stories around the campfire and led them in group singing. And when the boys went to their tents to sleep, he would go around to their cots and talk quietly to those who were homesick or frightened of the dark.

As always he saw with the eye of a doctor but recorded his impressions with the sensitivity of a writer. "The children were excited, enchanted, filled with wonder and delight," he wrote. "If there were clouds, they had a smile stretching across them; if there was anger, it was mild and only half serious because we worked together beautifully, teaching and helping each other. And all under the spell of the sun, green fields, and gold wheat-lands."

When the summer camp was ended he told each of the boys to feel free to come to the clinic at Warsaw to see him if ever he felt ill. Korczak delighted in this role of social worker, physician, and educator.

Back in Warsaw, Korczak attended a soiree at a temporary orphanage in a former convent at Franciszkanska Street, as the guest of the wife of Dr. Eliasberg. In those days in occupied Poland all institutions of a public character, ranging from municipal ambulances to soup kitchens, were supported and run by voluntary workers and contributions. This was true even of schools and hospitals, all of which were privately endowed. The children at Franciszkanska Street had formely been in another orphanage which had been run for personal gain by a corrupt supervisor. The children had been discovered living in louse-ridden filth and misery, and it was decided to move them into a temporary new home dedicated to Maria Konopnicka, a great Polish poetess.

When he arrived at the orphanage, the children were already entertaining the guests with songs and poetry recitations. He stood in the doorway alone until Mrs. Eliasberg noticed him. "I have a girl I want you to meet," she said, taking him by the hand. "You'll like her. She's my niece and her brother is Stanislau the engineer—he is married to my daughter. They met in France and his sister—the girl I want you to meet—has been to the best schools and studied social science in Switzerland and Belgium. And Henryk, she is also a Socialist."

Korczak protested that he was not eager to meet any girls, but it was too late. Mrs. Eliasberg's eyes were already searching the crowded room. She waved and Korczak saw a hand waving back.

"You'll see, you'll like her," promised Mrs. Eliasberg.

"And if I do," said Korczak, "must I pay you the usual fee of a matchmaker?"

"In this case it won't be necessary," said Mrs. Eliasberg, who clutched the hand of a plump girl with a round face, a full nose, and warm brown eyes framed by heavy black brows which gave her the look of a panda; she was so homely that she was almost attractive.

"This is Stefa Wilczynska," said Mrs. Eliasberg.

Korczak bowed.

"May I show you around the orphanage?" Stefa asked.

He offered Stefa his arm, and as they walked and talked he could see that she was cultured and well educated.

"Why are you here?" Korczak asked.

"My parents' home is next door to the orphanage at Swietojerska Street," she said. "One day I went in to visit the orphanage, thinking I might donate my services." Stefa laughed. "I thought I could give them something, but as I talked with the children I found that I needed them more than they needed me. Now I work here as assistant manager."

Korczak smiled and Stefa added defensively, "My brother is married to Dr. Eliasberg's daughter, are you thinking that's why I have the position?"

"No," said Korczak. "I was thinking of what you said about needing the children more than they needed you. I like that."

Later in the evening he bluntly asked Stefa why she wasn't married, since at that time it was rare to meet an unmarried twenty-two-year-old with parents who could afford a good dowry.

"You see me," said Stefa. "Am I such a beauty that a man would marry me for myself rather than my dowry?

Anyway, I want to drink vodka, I want to smoke cigarettes, to go to a university, cut my hair short and have a baby, husband or not."

Korczak laughed delightedly. She was quoting from one of his stories written in defense of the spinster.

"And like you, I am an assimilated Jew," said Stefa. "My brother and his wife became Christians. If I was orthodox I think my family could have married me off long ago."

Korczak was so impressed with the orphanage, and perhaps with Stefa, that he volunteered his services as a doctor, agreeing to be on call when needed.

The following summer he took poor children to camp again. This time he decided to keep note of the stories he told around the campfire. His stories were designed for two different audiences—Jewish or Christian children—and his notes gave him the basis for two lovely children's books, *Moski, Joseki and Srule* (popular names for Jewish children) and, *Joski, Janki and Franki* (popular names for Christian children).

The political situation in Poland was steadily worsening, and during the summer vacation Korczak heard for the first time complaints from the children about persecution. He recorded: "The quiet, commonplace Polish word used for 'sad' is 'smutno.' It is the same word in Jewish in sense, meaning, and effect. And when a Polish or Jewish child feels the weight of life the same word came to their minds—smutno."

The National Democrats began to dominate politics, and anti-Semitism was on the rise. In an article entitled

"Three Tides," published in 1910 in the journal *Societies,* Korczak wrote:

"First there is the tide of Polish Catholics, whose names end with the 'ski' and 'icz.' They say 'Let the bergs, the sohns, and the steins move to Franciszkanska Street, to the Jewish slums, to Solec. Let them give us nothing. Let them learn from us. . . .'

"Then there was the second tide, the Jewish descendants of the old established families, who do not wish to tolerate upstarts and who cling closely to their brothers of the Middle Ages. This tide says: 'To Solec with every ski and icz. We go to Krochmalna Street. You could learn a thing or two from your elder brothers, but there is nothing you can bestow on us.' "

And, said Korczak, there was the third tide. "Those of us who belong to the third tide say: 'We are sons of the same clay. Ages of mutual suffering and glittering success link us in a chain of the same mould. The same sun shines upon us, the same hail destroys our fields, the same earth hides the bones of our ancestors. There have been more tears than smiles in our history, but that was not our fault, and neither was it yours. Let us stick together, ski and berg, icz and sohn. . . .' As a Polish Jew I am nearest with my voice to your heart. I am nearest to the third tide. I am the third tide."

He had committed himself. He felt there was no other choice of action for himself as a Pole who was, coincidentally, a Jew. He had chosen sides: if the Poles made him a Jew he would be a Jew in their eyes but—and this was most important—he would remain a Pole in his own eyes. He withdrew from Socialist activities and cut himself off from his Gentile friends.

At the same time he expressed to other friends that he was disenchanted with the recognized authorities in his own field of medicine who, he believed, were far behind the times in their treatment of children. To him they seemed more concerned with developing bedside manners than new techniques for treating the sick; they were more interested in collecting fees than curing illnesses. He was distressed with the current books he had read on pedagogy. "What trash," he wrote. "It wasn't pedagogy. It was anthroposophy—the knowledge of man.

"It is a little sad," he wrote at this time. "Solitude is painful. But I have memories. School friends, pleasant gossip over a cup of coffee in a little café. . . . I do not seek more friends. I have made a deal with life, that we shall not interfere with each other. I have left off where it would have been disastrous to continue. In politics they call it a separation of influences."

While in this period of disillusionment with friends, country, and profession, Korczak was asked by Doctors Herz and Eliasberg to take over the directorship of a new orphanage. With the aid of contributions they had raised more than 110,000 rubles for construction of a new orphanage at Krochmalna Street which would be built according to his plans and ideas. He would be free to run the orphanage as he saw fit with Stefa Wilczynska as his assistant.

The new orphanage was built in 1911 and in the autumn of that year one hundred children moved from Franciszkanska Street to the handsome building at Krochmalna 92. It was named "Our Home."

A high iron fence in front and a brick wall along the sides and back enclosed the home, which was reached from the street through a wide gate. Pine trees shaded the cobblestone driveway circling a stone fountain set in grass. Korczak had planted the trees himself as a token of the continuity of life; at the orphanage's dedication he said that the children and trees would grow up together and would outlast him. From the street the building appeared to be all windows; there were thirty-six 5-foot tall windows on the front alone, because Korczak believed a child instinctively recognized a window as a symbol of light and freedom.

Inside the front door the visitor entered a two-story dining room and recreation hall. Although he had designed the building himself, this room was always a source of displeasure to Korczak: it was overlooked by a second-floor gallery which, he felt, made the big room seem too much like a penitentiary. When he walked along the balcony he felt like a warden in a prison. He feared the balcony suggested a lack of trust and confidence in the children.

The white-walled dormitories for the children were on the second and third floors of the building. Metal cots were situated in a cluster of four: two children slept head to toe with a wooden partition separating them from the other two. The dormitories were for sleeping only and children were allowed in them only at night. When they entered the dormitory they removed their shoes and walked in stocking feet on the polished oak floor.

Korczak lived in a glass cage rather like a lighthouse in the middle of the boy's dormitory. Hebrew teacher Jacob Tsouk recalls a light was always on in the doctor's room so that children could take comfort in the knowledge that he was "at home."

The children's lockers were on the first floor, next to the large and airy dining room. It was awkward for the children to have clothing and personal belongings on a floor other than the one on which they slept, but Korczak felt it kept them from having any excuse to visit the dormitories during the day.

Toilets were on either side of the stairs on the upper floors. Two large, white-enameled tubs in the basement were used every Friday night for bathing. Korczak himself helped carry hot water in buckets from the kitchen, and his supervision of each bath gave him an opportunity to check on a child's physical condition. Another basement room was his "cobbler's shop" where he repaired shoes and instructed new boys in the art of shining shoes.

Korczak performed all the duties of a father conscientiously. He pared fingernails, soothed wounded feelings, tended cuts and bruises, and administered cod-liver oil from huge bottles. He measured and weighed all the children at regular intervals and kept scrupulous pediatric records.

In 1912 the Polish press announced a Jewish boycott. National Democrats paraded in front of Jewish shops and businesses, forbidding people to buy. Homes and synagogues were burned. Jewish children were expelled from schools, and government employees were fired. The Jewish community was told it didn't belong in the new nation. Even Jews who had given up their religion, their customs, and their community were considered strangers in the land in which they were born.

Korczak opened the orphanage door one morning after a parade on Krochmalna Street and saw written on the door in black letters, DIRTY JEWS. Miss Stefa gasped, "Let me clean it off."

"No," said Korczak. "Let those who believe in the great Polish culture see it. Let them be ashamed."

3

In 1914 THE CONSTRUCTIVE ROUTINE OF KORCZAK'S LIFE was abruptly cut: he was called back into the Russian Army as a major in the Medical Corps. His first concern was to provide for the orphanage in his absence, so he hurried to the bank—one of Warsaw's largest—in which the orphanage had five thousand rubles on deposit. When he approached the manager and asked for the money to be released, he received instead a promise of twenty-five rubles. He protested angrily, saying he was leaving to serve in the army and the money was urgently needed for the upkeep of the orphanage. The manager reacted by stopping payment of the twenty-five rubles.

Furious but helpless, Korczak next went to the offices of his publisher, Jacub Mortkowicz. In the tradition of publishers with established authors, Mortkowicz was willing to advance money on the stipulation that he have an option on Korczak's next book. This was agreed, and Korczak was soon on his way to the front for the second time in less than a decade.

He was assigned again as a surgeon at a base hospital in Jerornia. There he devoted most of his off-duty time to writing. He devised a "Constitution and Declaration of Rights for Children" and worked out his system of self-government which he called "The Orphanage Statutes." He also worked on a book consolidating everything he had learned about teaching and working with children, which he called *How To Love a Child*.

While Korczak was stationed at Kiev, news reached the Polish colony there that there was an unusual doctor from Warsaw by the name of Henryk Goldszmidt with the Russian regiment. A Polish clerk in the local Russian administration invited Dr. Goldszmidt to visit with him. The conversation started stiffly in Russian, the official language, then the clerk discovered that Dr. Goldszmidt was also Janusz Korczak, whose writings he had admired for years. The conversation went on into the night in Polish, ending with a friendly handclasp and a promise on the clerk's part to see what he could do to make the doctor's life in Kiev pleasanter.

The clerk, who was a personage in the social circles of prerevolutionary Kiev, did do something. As a result of

218

his intervention Dr. Goldszmidt was transferred from his regiment to the Kiev garrison, where he was made responsible for three orphanages for Ukranian children. It was a busy time, as Korczak's diary describes it:

Kiev—chaos. Yesterday, the Bolsheviks. Today, the Ukranians. The Germans come nearer and nearer, and the whole of Russia is believed to be in turmoil, although it is officially still Czarist. For six months I was the doctor to three orphanages near Kiev. Murders were an everyday affair and excited no comment. How naïve my efforts look when seen through the perspective of the years. I tried to organize and expand. From a sober sense of duty I tried to save the children.

Children were covered with ulcers and scabs. Their eyes were sore. They were ill as the results of malnutrition and maltreatment. There was no one to look after them. They were hungry. The authorities allocated to the orphanages an instructress of embroidery!

To this day I cannot shake off the prejudices and disgust I then built up within me towards certain authoritative elements. My objections and protests made them uncomfortable. The same revolver that was used to shoot sick horses was pointed at me, as a warning that I was in the wrong places at the wrong times. Graft, robbery! Human language has not invented terms strong enough to denounce the situation.

In addition to working at the three orphanages he also helped out at a boarding school in Kiev for unruly Polish boys run by Mrs. Maryna Falska. An active Socialist, she had been deported to Russia from Poland in 1900 for publishing an article in an underground socialist newspaper. After three years of bitter exile she had returned and taken over the school.

Korczak helped Mrs. Falska establish workshops where the boys learned shoemaking, tailoring, bookbinding, and plumbing. Here he tried out for the first time the system of self-government he had devised. Pupils not only made their own rules for running the school but enforced discipline with their own court of justice.

The grateful Polish colony in Kiev hired an attic room to make Korczak more comfortable, but he worried constantly about Krochmalna 92. Once he went along to an inexpensive eating house, ordered tripe, and "cried his eyes out" because it reminded him of Warsaw. He made no effort to disguise the fact that he yearned to be released from the army.

Eventually he mustered the courage to write to the garrison commandant asking to be discharged. To his joy he was given his demobilization papers and allowed to return to Warsaw.

When his train finally pulled into the station, he sent his baggage on to his mother's home and walked alone, for the first time in almost four years, savoring the sights, sounds, and smells of his native city. On the Iron Gate Square the lights were already burning, and people thronged the market stalls. Storekeepers presided over tubs of butter, huge cheeses, baskets of mushrooms, trays of fish, each with its own heady fragrance. He passed a brightly lit slaughterhouse; porters hosing down the bloodied stone floor reminded him of the front-line hospitals he had recently left.

He hailed a droshky and gave the driver his mother's

address. A friend had written that she was ill and told everyone she dreamed and longed for only one thing: "To live until the day of Henryk's return." Finally he was there and in his mother's arms. The loving old woman spread her admiration under his feet like a soft carpet. He basked in the warm and endless waves of homage, and for long hours he told her of his life during the war. She caressed his hand with a blissful smile no matter what horrors he described: she heard only the sound of his voice, not the words he spoke.

As a condition of his discharge he had to remain as a medical officer in the newly established Polish Forces, spending several hours a day in the hospital for infectious diseases in Lodz, then in Warsaw. He would be able to visit Krochmalna Street two or three times a week. His mother pleaded with him to stay with her and he agreed, because it would enable him to sleep without the frequent interruptions of the orphanage.

The next day in the courtyard of the orphanage a moving reception awaited him. The children had been scrubbed and dressed in clean clothes. In honor of the returning hero they were arranged in military formation in front of the orphanage behind Stefa in a clean apron, hair tied neatly in a bun, her eyes smiling.

Many of the children were new, but he was already a legend to them. Dr. Eliasberg preceded him through the gate into the yard. Korczak followed shyly, the army uniform looking incongruous on his slight, stooped figure. He shook Stefa's hand, then smiled at the children and asked why they were standing so quietly. "We should be playing," he said. The doctor was back home and with those words life resumed its old routine.

Late in 1919 Korczak acquired a farm named Little Rose in Goclawek, a settlement of summer villas and small cottages on the Vistula. He hoped to start a communal farm for the older boys which would be self-sustaining.

At the same time he was busy organizing a new orphanage for Christians, to accommodate the children of workers unable to support their families and the orphans of soldiers killed during the war.

By the end of the year the first fifty children were moved into the new home located in a building on Cedrowa Street in Pruskov, near Warsaw. Mrs. Falska came from Kiev to take charge of the new institution which, in the beginning, had no benches or tables for school or dining room, no fuel for stoves, and only a small supply of food. There was not even money enough for colored paper from which toys could be made.

The community rallied to Korczak's aid. One person told him, "I know where some beds are to be had." Another told him, "I'll write a letter—I know where to get some firewood." A third said, "Run quickly to my shop. I have some flour left. Get it before it is sold out."

Sometimes Korczak himself queued up in the cold for hours for potatoes, then hastened back to the orphanage to warm up before standing in a long line again to obtain some other necessity.

Writing of the hardships and the community cooperation of those days Korczak said, "In this fashion, given a practical lesson from life and observing life's difficulties,

222

children learned gratitude. They learned to accept their duties, and the virtues of collaboration, solidarity, and help, without resorting to capricious moods or demands."

In addition to his work at the two orphanages he also appeared in Warsaw District Court as an expert on juvenile crimes, lectured at the Warsaw School of Science and the Institute of Specialized Pedagogy, and worked at the hospital for infectious diseases.

The hospital had many typhus patients, and Korczak was constantly tired and underfed. One day he fell ill at his mother's house, and the diagnosis was typhus. His mother nursed him, but she contracted the disease while he was still in a coma. Within a week she was dead.

Her body was carried out of the apartment at night so neither he nor the neighbors would know of her death. The secret was kept until Korczak recovered. When he discovered the truth he blamed himself for her death. His feeling of guilt was so great that one day while still convalescent he went to her grave, in the Warsaw Jewish cemetery, a vial of morphine tablets in his pocket. He was found unconscious by her headstone: he hadn't taken enough morphine to kill himself.

The rabbi who had performed services for his mother came to talk with him, to offer him peace. Korczak was an unbeliever, and the meeting between the two men was strained. After a long silence he asked the rabbi, "Am I guilty of her death?"

"You are not guilty," said the rabbi firmly.

"Can one speak with the dead?" asked Korczak.

The rabbi trembled. "It says in the Book of the Multitudes of the Dead, 'Think but rightly of one who has died, and he is there. You may summon him inwardly, and he must come; hold him, and he must remain. Think of him in love or hate, he feels it. Think of him in stronger love or in stronger hate, he feels it more strongly. In every festival that you dedicate to the dead, they arise; they flutter around every image you consecrate to them, listen to every word that tells of them.'"

"Can I speak with her?" asked Korczak.

"Be pure and she will have peace," said the rabbi. "When you soar to the Third World she will bathe there in the sea of the Third World with you."

Korczak fell silent, and finally the rabbi left. All during the day Korczak ate nothing, drank nothing. At last, at nightfall, he broke into tears and raised his voice to the God in which he had no faith. He cried, "How have I offended You? That in this hour of need I cannot find You! When my feet are entangled in thorns and my heart is bleeding . . . I called for You. And I am alone."

He tried to summon up a vision of his mother but his only vision was of children. He took this as a sign that if there was a meaning to her death and his continued existence, it was the children. He could not abandon life until he had completed the task he had set for himself.

He ordered the inscription for his mother's tombstone: "I have not forgotten your commandments, neither have I transgressed them."

When he went back to the orphanage he had changed. He realized that if a lonely man needed something spiritual to hold onto in desperate times, a loney child's need must be even greater. He composed a special prayer for the children to say at mealtimes, thanking the Lord for the food they were to eat. He dedicated a book of prayers, *Alone with God,* to his parents. And he arranged for the Jewish children to have religious instruction if they wished it. He used to call children to prayer by playing a few notes on a flute. Lessons and prayers were conducted in the orphanage dining room. If Korczak happened to come in the room during prayer time, he would pinch the bridge of his nose and act as if he, too, were praying.

Coupled with his concern for the spiritual needs of the children was Korczak's conception of children as individuals who should be treated with respect and dignity. His pioneering concepts, combined with his ability to crystallize his thoughts in lucid and interesting articles and books, soon established him as one of the foremost educators in Poland. By the late twenties his reputation had spread across the Baltic states to Germany and the English-speaking lands. Educators from all over the world came to visit the orphanage at Krochmalna Street, and there was always a waiting list of students who wished to work with him.

One of his innovations was a weekly newspaper published in each orphanage called *The Orphanage Gazette.* Contributions were dropped into a box, and since the orphanages had no printing facilities the gazettes were handwritten and read aloud every Friday night. The newspaper was then posted on a bulletin board for the following week.

The gazettes became an important feature of orphanage life and its reading was an eagerly anticipated event. Korczak was not surprised at the children's enthusiasm; he

225

had always believed there was a place even in adult newspapers for a special children's section.

Then in 1926 a respected Warsaw newspaper, *Our Review*, a Jewish daily in the Polish language, gave Korczak a free hand in organizing and editing a supplement for children called *The Little Review*. At Korczak's insistence, young contributors received honoraria. Children who were permanent members of the editorial staff had their own desks and were permitted to avail themselves of the newspaper's stenographic service. When a young boy, recruited to run the puzzle corner called "Brain Teasers," said he didn't think he was bright enough, Korczak told him he had been given the job just because he wasn't exceptional.

"I loathe people who are too competent," Korczak said.

During its first year *The Little Review* had more than two hundred correspondents on the staff and more than nine thousand letters. The supplement became the champion of children's rights, to the annoyance of many adults. Korczak was the only adult contributor, and his witty and sharp style provided an enlightening yet critical commentary on happenings of the day. Frequently he entered into correspondence with contributors and always taught them with patience, good humor, and tolerance.

Aided by the fame of *The Little Review*, Korczak's reputation as an educator and expert on children continued to grow. Early in 1935, as "The Old Doctor," he was engaged to give lectures on child-raising and children's problems on the radio. In a short time his ideas and his warm, friendly voice earned him a large audience. Less than a year after he went on the air, however, he was fired for making a statement that offended the anti-Semitic leaders of the Polish government. At almost the same time he received a much harder blow. After a stormy meeting with the governing body of the Christian orphanage at Bielany, he resigned from the board of directors.

Korczak was not easily defeated, but this double blow coming just before his sixtieth birthday was almost more than he could handle. He became ill. After long weeks of depression he decided to seek refuge and change in Palestine.

In July 1936 he arrived as an honored guest at the Kibbutz Eyn Harod. Eyn Harod is deep in the Valley of Israel, across from the mountain where Gideon selected his soldiers and King Saul was buried. Cool breezes from Lake Harod move softly across the land, and birds sing in the eucalyptus and pine trees.

Korczak was delighted to find Jews in the role of peasants tilling the soil. In Poland this was a rare sight: Jews lived in cities and by ancient tradition were forbidden to farm the land. In Palestine the plough, saw, and ax replaced the snobbery of diplomas.

He visited Joseph Heilpern, a former student, at Kibbutz Eyn Hamifratz in the northern part of Palestine. The two spent hours discussing the advantages and disadvantages of collectivism and communal life. "Although he was not a political Zionist, after many disappointments Korczak was quite sure that the only place for the Jewish child was in Palestine," Heilpern recalled.

Toward the end of his visit Korczak saw another former student, Yaacov Ben Joseph, at Tel Adashim, a

227

kibbutz near Afulah in the Israel Valley. "I must go back to my children in the orphanage," the doctor said. "If it wasn't for them I would stay here."

When Korczak returned to Poland after six weeks in Israel, he found the Nazi power even more threatening, and Polish anti-Semitism rising with it. It was not necessary to be a strategist to see what lay ahead: the Jews in Poland were abandoned and helpless. Korczak tried to convince himself that he was resigned to the impending war and to the plight of the Jews, and that he had long ago made peace with the idea of death. But in truth he was full of fear, and when he had to be on the streets late at night he walked hurriedly in the shadows.

In a letter to Joseph Heilpern, written soon after his return to Warsaw, he said, "After a period of depression, lasting for a few months, I have decided to go out and spend the last few years of my life in Palestine. I have decided on a year in Jerusalem to learn Hebrew so that I can enter the life of a kibbutz.

"My trip should materialize within a month, as I cannot remain here much longer in this state of uncertainty. So, more or less in May, I shall be on the high seas. To decide was most difficult. I would like to be sitting already in a small, quiet room in Jerusalem, with the Bible, a Hebrew dictionary, pencil and paper. There I would live after the manner of a student in poverty. The only thing left to me then would be contemplation . . . the last of my life's difficult trials . . . the finding out of why . . ."

But the habit of responsibility is not so easily broken, and soon he wrote to Heilpern again: "I have broken all ties here. Only a handful of friends remain. But the idea that I should run away . . . is unthinkable. I do not want to break contact with Polish reality. I would be haunted by every call of every orphan I left behind. I want to tie what is today with everything that is of yesterday and tomorrow. A pity, but I could not do otherwise. If I left, I would never forgive myself. I detest desertion. My vocabulary does not allow it. So be it."

On September 29, 1941, Korczak wrote to Zylberberg, "For many reasons we would like to celebrate Rosh Hashanah and Yom Kippur in our orphanage, but on the other hand we are told that the services, which should be solemn, might turn out to be meaningless and muddled. Could you help us?"

It was typical of Korczak to write a letter even though he lived only a door away from Zylberberg. Korczak was gentle enough to believe in putting such requests in writing so that a person who wished to refuse might do so without the embarrassment of a face-to-face confrontation.

Zylberberg was delighted to help, however, and he responded by sending Korczak a shortened service, which Korczak further adapted by arranging for a song to be introduced to lighten the service for children who did not understand Hebrew.

The innovation was a success at Passover, which was celebrated at the orphanage by Korczak with twelve of his older boys and a handful of friends, including Zylberberg and Adam Czerniakow, head of the Judenrat.

The guests were surprised to find Korczak participating in the service wearing a black skullcap. With the others he humbly turned to the God of his ancestors with the

229

age-old prayer that had a special significance for the Jews faced with disaster.

A few days later Korczak met Myron Zylberberg in the courtyard. Zylberberg was terribly depressed and his eyes were red-rimmed from tears. "My wife is in the eleventh day of typhus and Dr. Grimberg doesn't want to come see her," he told Korczak. "She's dying."

"Why didn't you ask me to come?" Korczak asked.

"Because of the children."

Korczak nodded. "Don't worry," he said, "I will see if I can help." The two men went into Zylberberg's apartment where Henrietta lay on a couch, her face flushed with fever, her body wet with perspiration. Korczak examined her carefully, then admitted that she was indeed near death. "But," he said, "if she manages to survive the night you have won the battle."

Mrs. Zylberberg survived the night. The next morning, when Zylberberg told the good news to Korczak, the doctor said, "You see, you at least have won the war."

Even in the ghetto Korczak tried to maintain the formal routines he had long ago established for the orphanage. On Saturday the Children's Court still met, and before that he held a staff meeting, with reports from his assistants and representatives of the children. At one such meeting he called on Zylberberg for a report. "I am prepared to listen, not to talk," said Zylberberg.

"Talk about anything you wish," said Korczak.

Zylberberg was embarrassed, but he decided to tell the group about a book he had recently read, *The Forty Days of Musa Dagh* by Franz Werfel. One of the most popular books in the ghetto, it was the story of a doctor who abandoned his patients to save his own life.

When Zylberberg finished telling the story, Korczak spoke abruptly. "That will never happen to me."

✡

✡   BOOK THREE   ✡

✡

1

Only a few days before the Nazi Aktion started, Korczak sent invitations to his friends and possible donors to attend a production of Rabindranath Tagore's "The Post Office," a play which had been forbidden by the German censors.

The invitation sent to friends of the orphanage as well as the children and staff of the Dzielna Street orphanage and the ladies from CENTOS, read: "We are convinced that there is about to be a culmination to the beautiful story. It is about to reach the highest step on the ladder of feeling and sentiment of which we human beings are capable. We, therefore, beg you to accept this invitation for Saturday, 18 July 1942, at 4:30 P.M."

The invitation was supplemented by the poem of the ghetto poet, Wladyslaw Szengel:

"Something more than the text—the mood.

"Something more than emotion—the experience.

"Something more than actors—the children."

The two-act play directed by Esther Winogron was put on in an upstairs room converted to a theater. The play's frail little Indian boy, condemned to seclusion and inaction by ill health, was played by the violinist, Abrasha, who brought such sincerity and reality to the delicate transition from life to death that the audience sobbed without restraint.

Korczak himself listened tensely. He was very pale. Asked later why he had chosen this particular play, he answered, "I would like my children to learn how to receive with dignity and peace the Angel of Death."

But even after the Jewish policeman's warning, Korczak was still not prepared for the end. He had the feeling he had observed among soldiers, that others would be shot but not him. He never stopped believing there would be a miracle: something would happen to save his orphans.

On the morning of August 5 he was sitting at his desk trying to write when at 4:30 A.M. Michael Wroblewski, Davidek, Yankelek, and Monius the Elder left the orphanage to go to their job of tightening the wall around the ever-shrinking ghetto. Wroblewski, who had worked at the Krochmalna Street home in the thirties, was supervisor on the project, and the boys had volunteered for the job to earn extra food rations.

Wroblewski asked Korczak about rumors he had heard that the orphanage was to be evacuated. "I am certain the Germans will take more groups away to labor camps," said Korczak, his eyes red and tired. "But why should they bother with the children? They are too small to work."

The two men said good-bye in the doorway of the Home. Korczak returned to his diary.

"The appearance of a normal morning. I say to Hannia, 'Good morning.' I beg of her, 'Smile.' And I see the sick, pale, tired faces."

"Our Father who art in heaven . . . A prayer made by hunger and wretchedness. Our daily bread . . . Bread. They sold their belongings and clothing for a litre of oil. A kilo of groats for a glass of schnapps . . .

"I water the flowers. My bald head is visible at the window. A good target. He has a rifle. Why does he stand there so quietly, watching. He has received no orders. Perhaps in civil life he was a village schoolmaster. A solicitor or a road sweeper in Leipzig. A waiter in Cologne. What would he do if I nodded at him? Or waved a friendly hand? Perhaps he does not even know that things are—as they are. My distant friend since yesterday . . ."

While he was writing, military squads of Jewish policemen and Ukranian and Latvian militiamen under the command of SS squad leaders had begun patrolling the southeastern edges of the small ghetto. The scattered patrols had been moving leisurely and seemingly purposelessly along Wielka, Sosnova, Sliska, and Zlota Streets. One of the patrols halted a young man who, perhaps fearing he would be pressed into a labor battalion, bolted. He was shot by the squad leader.

At 8 A.M. SS Obersturmfuehrer Klostermayer, in charge of the morning's operation, stationed himself in front of the orphanage and blew his whistle twice. Soldiers who had reached their prearranged positions on schedule fanned out the entire length of the four streets, sealing the block to be evacuated. One man every thirty paces; each soldier in visual contact with the man on his left and right.

When Korczak heard the two sharp blasts and saw the German sentry outside his window click his heels and snap to attention, he put down his pen. Time had run out.

Obersturmfuehrer Klostermayer, accompanied by half a dozen Jewish policemen and three Ukranians carrying guns slung casually over their shoulders, marched into the courtyard. A squad leader bellowed, "Alle Juden raus, alle Juden hinunter."

Korczak quickly removed his green apron and hung it on a peg behind the door of his room. He rushed to open the front door.

The nattily dressed SS officer and the old Jew in the faded uniform studied each other for a moment.

"I have a request," said Korczak, speaking first.

"You are an officer?" Klostermayer asked.

"Yes, a major."

"What do you want then, Jewish Major?" Klostermayer asked with heavy irony, glancing at the soldiers near him for a reaction to his small joke.

"I have been promised that I will lead my children, not one of your men," said Korczak. "The children will be frightened if it is done any other way. I am their guardian and they will follow me. If you don't trust me, my bald head is a good target."

Klostermayer smiled. "Very well," he said. "Permission granted. The main thing is to see that it all goes off smoothly. We will bring up at the sides and the rear, not the front.

"Everyone—adult or child—is allowed to take one small suitcase containing valuables and a change of clothes. Nothing else is to be taken. Your building is to be emptied in fifteen minutes; everyone out front here ready to go. We have a schedule to keep."

Korczak went into the dining room where the children were finishing their breakfast of potato soup. Clapping his hands for attention, he apologized for interrupting their meal. "But," he explained, "we are going to the country sooner than I expected. We leave in fifteen minutes. Go to your lockers at once, put on your best clothes and pack a small bag or rucksack with your valuables. The younger children can bring a toy or two. Be outside in the courtyard promptly in ten minutes."

As the children went off to their lockers Abrasha stayed behind. "Is music allowed where we are going?" he asked. Korczak answered, "Music is allowed. Bring your violin."

Stefa, too, was waiting to talk but she could only sob. "The time has come," said Korczak. "Tell Sabina,

239

Natalia and the other teachers that we are allowed to take one small suitcase and all our courage. We must be calm."

Hanka Faynar arrived at the orphanage for her daily visit with her brother Nussen as the children began assembling in the courtyard. Nussen, wearing clean shorts and shirt, ran to her side. Excitedly he blurted out his good news. "We are going for a treat to the camp at Goclawek."

Hanka was a ghetto child, and she knew what the soldiers in the courtyard meant. She found Korczak in the center of the courtyard busying himself with some of the younger children, buttoning the coat of one, tying up the package of another. She tugged on his jacket and pulled him to one side.

"Why did you tell Nussen and the others that they were going for a treat?" she asked. "You know that isn't the truth."

"The children don't need to know where they are going," Korczak said firmly. "They should sing and be happy. You must leave quickly. I don't want Nussen to see you crying."

Korczak led Hanka by the hand out of the courtyard, explaining to Klostermayer that she was not one of his orphans but a visitor. Hanka fled into the street just as Klostermayer ordered three Jewish policemen to search the building. Anyone found inside would be shot on the spot.

A quarter of a century later one of the Jewish policemen remembered the event vividly.

240

Our lives depended on the thoroughness of our search. One never knew when Klostermayer might decide to search the house after us. Anyone found hiding would be instantly shot. And then we would be.

It was my job to search the rooms other than the dormitories. I opened the bathroom door and started to search the room. Then I heard a sound behind me. I turned and a boy was standing there, a bayonet in his hand pointed at my throat. It was ridiculous. A grown man face-to-face with a boy who couldn't have been bar mitzvah, but I have never been so frightened.

"One sound and I will kill you," the boy said. His eyes never left mine. "If you tell the Germans that I am in here they will kill you because you didn't bring me out. If they come after me I will kill one of them, I promise you. You know the consequences."

The boy pushed the tip of the bayonet lightly into my throat. What he said made sense. I had a tiger by the tail. I could only hope that this would be one time Klostermayer did not search. I shouted to the others, "All clear," knowing that the boy would have buried the bayonet in my back if I gave a warning.

When I got outside I joined the others in reporting that the building was empty. Luckily, Klostermayer had his hands full with two hundred children milling about. He did not search the building. Since then I often wondered who the boy was and what happened to him.

Klostermayer ordered the other families occupying the building to stand on one side of the courtyard while the children lined up five abreast in a column. A Ukranian was told to count them.

There were 192 children and 8 adults: Korczak; Stefa;

Henryk Asterblum, the orphanage bookkeeper; Balbina Feliksowa Grzyb, instructor and wife of Felek, Korczak's secretary who had gone off on business for the day; Sabina Ljzerowicz, seamstress; Natalia Poz, teacher; Rosa Stockman, who worked in the kitchen and was the mother of Romcia; and Dora Solnicka, the Home's treasurer.

The adults wore heavy clothes. The women had their hair up in kerchiefs. Stefa was wearing a shapeless jumper. The only adult male other than Korczak was Asterblum, who carried his meager belongings in a pillowcase. Like Korczak he was hatless. Korczak was the only one without luggage. He had even left his eyeglasses on his desk. When he asked Klostermayer for permission to go back into the house for them it was refused.

The children's wooden-soled shoes made a clattering noise as they hurried from the building, then stood in the courtyard impatiently waiting to begin their trip. Many of the girls were wearing dresses made from the same bolts of cloth.

Some of the younger children carried beach toys or sand pails. Hannia carefully packed in her purse the precious picture of her mother. A few of the older children carried rucksacks slung over their shoulders with clothing, personal belongings, or books. Abrasha, carrying his precious violin, had struggled into the crowd to get a place next to Regina. Everyone was wearing a Jewish armband.

When Klostermayer saw Abrasha's violin case he asked him to play a tune while the children lined up. "I don't remember what the boy played but it was terrible," the

242

Jewish policeman said. "There was a string or two missing from his violin. He had only played a couple of minutes when Klostermayer said, 'Put the violin away, Jew boy. We leave now.'"

Hanka Faynar, who was hidden in a doorway across the street, saw the group march from the courtyard. Korczak was at the head of the procession holding Nussen's hand and carrying his godchild, five-year-old Romcia Stockman, who was crying. Musik was next to Korczak carrying the orphanage banner. Mrs. Stefa was at the end of the line, which was surrounded on both sides by soldiers and policemen.

The streets near the orphanage had been cleared, but the sidewalks were packed with the occupants of all the neighboring houses. During the Aktion all occupants of houses in the immediate area had to stand in front of their homes or shops; a terrifying experience because the SS frequently selected people at random to join the evacuees. The crowd of spectators was strangely still and motionless. No one wanted to call attention to himself.

"During the first week of the evacuation a parent or relative of someone in a group would scream or try to join us," the Jewish policeman said. "The SS had orders to shoot such people. Usually the crowd cooperated in quieting or holding back people who would have made a protest or caused trouble.

"What I remember most about the marches was the feeling of eyes—there were eyes everywhere. It was as if the whole city was a giant eye staring at us. I still have nightmares about that."

Even before the echo of the wooden shoes had died

away on the street the looters came, more than half a hundred of them. The first wave was made up of professionals who made a precarious living by following evacuation squads and waiting until an area had been cleared. Then they searched quickly and expertly, rifled the cupboards, slit mattresses and bags with sharp knives, looking for valuables.

The second wave consisted of Jews from the immediate neighborhood whose needs were more simple. Starving, they snatched at a half-eaten crust of bread, gulped the dregs of coffee left in cups, fought over a tattered blanket. Adziu, the bayonet hidden in the waistband of his trousers, mingled with the frenzied looters and disappeared.

Within five minutes the orphanage was devastated, littered by fragments of clothing, papers, and luggage. An employee of the Jewish Kehilla, one of the many ghetto charitable organizations, who had heard of the Aktion looked in. He saw there was still some bedding left and rushed to his office on Grzybowska Street to make a report.

Fourteen-year-old Irena Szereszewska who was a student at a school nearby heard the orphans coming long before she saw them. "When they passed me I thought from their attitude they were going on an excursion," she remembers. "In a way I envied them." Irena ran to tell her mother who was working at the Jewish Kehilla the news: Korczak's orphanage was en route to the Umschlagplatz.

Korczak's old friend and neighbor, Myron Zylberberg, was in the basement of a house at Novolipky and Smocza,

244

a few blocks from the orphanage. "I saw the procession quite by accident. They were walking in a long column, moving quite slowly with Korczak at the head of the line.

"It was unusual because the SS were not beating and shoving the children as they normally did with other groups being moved out of the ghetto. I heard occasional shouts of 'Schnell' and 'Tempo' but the soldiers were not rough. The children looked normal, as if quite confident to be walking behind Korczak, and he appeared calm during the time I could see him."

The group of orphans marched half a kilometer to the Catholic Church at All Saints Square, arriving there a little after 9:00 A.M. Thousands of other Jews who were to be evacuated that day had been gathered in the street.

Standing on the church steps under the statue of a saint whose head had been blown off was sixteen-year-old Janina Brandweyn, who had been working in a glove shop next to the church when an SS man ordered the shop emptied and its occupants lined up on the street.

Janina saw Korczak leading the children and anxiously tried to see if Halinka, one of her friends, was in the group. "Thousands of people were in the crowd being marched by," Janina said. "The Ukranians had whips and every few minutes the Germans would shout 'Schnell' and the Ukranians would begin to beat people. Some people tripped and fell and their luggage spilled open, tripping others. Those who fell were shot by the SS if they did not get up quickly enough. But Korczak's group seemed to be marching by itself! The SS were merely walking alongside. I never saw Halinka."

At the Jewish Kehilla no one was aware of the Aktion

then taking place. Helena Szereszewska, Irena's mother, who kept a diary of her life in the ghetto, recorded that she was standing at a file cabinet when an employee she didn't know rushed into the building, red-faced and breathing hard as if he had been running. "He looked as though he wanted to say something important and everyone gathered around him. When he finally got his breath back, he said, 'What shall we do with the stores of underwear, bedding, and clothing that is left in Korczak's orphanage? Tell me. What shall we do with them?' We were all stunned."

Minutes later Helena's daughter arrived and confirmed the news. "We didn't know what to do," Mrs. Szereszewska said years later, "Today it was their turn, tomorrow it would be ours."

One person did know what to do, however. Wladyslaw Friedheim, General Secretary of CENTOS, was in his office when a clerk who had been on the roof of the building rushed in to say that Korczak and the children were being evacuated. Friedheim immediately sent a messenger to Dr. Gustav Wrelikowski, who had connections with Dr. Hans Franck, Governor General of Poland, and Dr. Ludwik Fisher, the District Governor of Warsaw. The message read: "Korczak and children being evacuated today. We must do something."

After the miserable group of Jews left the blockaded area around the church square, they marched through streets that were absolutely deserted. The neighbors of evacuees had to stand on the sidewalk, but in the rest of the ghetto no one dared show his face when an Aktion was under way in the area. "The Latvians and Ukranians

246

would shoot anyone they saw peeking out of a window," said Jonas Turkow, who lived at the corner of Novolipky and Smocza. "When I heard the sound of a group being marched by my house I stood far to one side of a window in the shade of the room and looked out, hoping I wouldn't see anyone I knew. This time I saw Korczak and the children going by slowly. It was hot and they were obviously tired, but Korczak looked untroubled and seemed to be making jokes with some of the younger children."

It was 1½ kilometers through the heart of the small ghetto to the Chlodna Street bridge which linked it with the large ghetto. It was getting hot: the weather at noon was a muggy 84 degrees. It must have been torture for the children to walk, trying to hurry, on the uneven cobblestones. Witnesses say they stumbled, fell, and the wooden shoes blistered their feet. By the time they reached the bridge with its seventy steep steps many must have been near the end of their strength.

"I will never forget the scene on the bridge steps," the Jewish policeman said. "The smaller children had to be shoved up the steps to the top. Below us on Chlodna Street were hundreds of jeering Poles, yelling, 'Good-bye, Jews.' Many of the children fell or were pushed down the steps on the other side."

Korczak, exhausted and anguished, refused to be daunted. At the corner of Dzielna and Karmelicka he called Klostermayer to him and said, "We could save a lot of time by turning west here."

"Why?" asked the puzzled German.

"Because the Jewish cemetery is less than three blocks away."

Michael Wroblewski returned to the orphanage at midday with Davidek, Yankelek, and Monius. "The house was devastated, as if a typhoon had hit it," he recalled. "I couldn't believe that a few hours before all had been in order. The boys started to cry. We were all feeling helpless. After half an hour of despair I told the boys to get busy—to find any of the doctor's personal papers which were still around and bring them to me."

Wroblewski himself went to Korczak's small bedroom. The doctor's apron was still on the peg behind the door; his eyeglasses with the cracked lens were still on the desk. But everything else was a shambles. He found that the doctor's suitcase filled with personal papers had been cut open, then discarded as worthless. There were stacks of material including graphs of the growth and weight of every child in Korczak's care over the years, material he had hoped to publish. The suitcase also included the doctor's handwritten last will and testament.

"I packed everything I could find, all I judged was important, in the suitcase and tied it up with string," Wroblewski said. "Then I took the boys to the home of Felek Grzyb by the large ghetto bridge. And I sent the material by messenger to Igor Newerly Abramov."

After two hours of impatient waiting Wladyslaw Friedheim finally got a message back from Dr. Wrelikowski, who said he had implored the two German officials to get Korczak released. Their answers read: "The Judenrat can have Korczak but not the children. We are issuing an order to that effect immediately."

248

By then Korczak and the children had almost reached the Umschlagplatz. Zvi Wasser, secretary for the diarist Emanuel Ringleblum and a reporter for the underground press, was in the shop of the Brothers Landau when he saw the orphans in the stream of four to five thousand people pouring down Zamenhofa Street toward the Umschlagplatz gate, which was about twenty meters east of the shop.

"They were walking slowly," Wasser said. "I had the strange thought that it was a shame that on such a nice sunny day Korczak and the children had to go to their death."

Halinka Pinchonson's mother worked as a nurse in the first aid station by the loading area. (The staff was permitted to revive those who had fainted or were slightly injured, but seriously ill people were taken out by the back door and shot.) When Mrs. Pinchonson heard that Korczak's orphans had arrived at the Umschlagplatz she fought her way through the crowds to her daughter's side. She took the girl's hand and dragged her to the steps of the first aid building.

"I have a place to hide you here during the nights and I can protect you during the days," she told Halinka.

"But why, Mummy?" asked Halinka. "I want to go with the other children to camp."

"I don't want you to go," said Mrs. Pinchonson. "I want you to stay here with me."

"I don't want to leave Dr. Korczak," Halinka said firmly. "When things were bad you asked him to take care of me just as he took care of you. He is my other father. You have always said that. I want to stay with him."

The argument ended abruptly. An SS man wrenched Halinka from her mother's grasp.

The Umschlagplatz was crowded with the thousands of Jews scheduled for that morning's resettlement to the East. They were carrying their most valued possessions in pillowcases or sheets made into sacks and tied with ropes and balanced on their shoulder, half the load in front and half in back.

"It was hell, impossible to describe, just hell," said the Jewish policeman who had escorted the orphanage. "Klostermayer ordered another count of the children. Then their stars were snipped off and thrown into the center of the courtyard. It looked like a field of buttercups."

The air was sticky with humidity and the closeness of unwashed bodies. The stench was unbearable: there were no toilets and people relieved themselves wherever they could find space. Human dignity had ceased to exist.

Shots were fired at random by the Ukranians and Latvians. Every shot hit a target. A woman standing near the orphans slipped down onto the stones, killed by a stray shot. A child screamed, "Mother, mother." With the timing of an expert in such matters a Latvian guard waited until the scene had reached a high point, then he raised his revolver and fired. A man cradled the dead pair in his arms. He reached in his pocket and in front of everyone took poison. No one interfered.

Then there were shouts from the SS. Whips snapped. The doors of the waiting freight cars were tugged open

250

by the Jewish police. The smell of the chloride of lime used to disinfect the trains was overpowering.

In the midst of the chaos an SS officer beat his way through the crowd and handed Korczak a letter. No one knows what the two men said or what the letter contained, although Wladyslaw Friedheim believes it was the promised offer to let Korczak return home—alone.

Wooden ramps were placed leading into the railroad cars. Guards began to shove and pummel the crowd toward the ramps. Those who fell or were pushed off the ramps were picked up and thrown bodily into the open cars.

"Korczak entered the freight car first, followed by the youngest children," the Jewish policeman said. "Mrs. Stefa and the rest went into the next car."

One of those who survived embarkation from the Umschlagplatz is certain that once the sliding doors had closed, Korczak would have stood blinking, his limbs numb, and then he would have done as thousands before him did. He would join the others in an anguished scream of *Help,* hoping at this last hour to stir the conscience of the world.

At 12:55 the train left on schedule for Treblinka.

On the evening of August 5, 1942, Untersturmfuehrer Erwin Schneider was found dead in his quarters. A Luger pistol, a gift from his uncle when he graduated from the National Political Training School at Schleswig-Holstein, was clutched in his hand. He left no note. He was officially reported as "Killed in Action."

✡

✡ **EPILOGUE** ✡

✡

THE EXACT DATE AND MANNER OF THE DEATH OF JANUSZ Korczak and his orphans is not known. Thorough as they were in the matter of mass murder, the Germans kept no records of names of those who passed through the gas chambers. Only of numbers. On August 5—6,783; 6—10,085; 7—10,672; 8—7,304. During the month of August, 135,120 were exterminated at Treblinka.

In one corner of the camp, the earth contained 700,000 bodies weighing approximately 35,000 tons, with a volume of 90,000 cubic meters. Undoubtedly Korczak and his children account for some small part of those statistics.

But as General Hahn had feared, Korczak became a martyr, one of the sparks which fired the revolt. "Remember Korczak's orphans" became a rallying cry; a spur to prod the remaining Jews in the ghetto who refused to believe that they, too, were doomed to extermination.

Just two weeks after the orphanage was evacuated, the first blow of the resistance movement was struck. On August 21, 1942, Israel Kanal loaded the Luger pistol, the contribution of the Polish Socialists, and assassinated the Jewish police chief Jozef Szerynski. His successor, Jacob Laikin, was also killed. Assassins' bullets struck down policemen, informers, and collaborators. Judenrat chairman Marek Lichtenbaum, who replaced Czerniakow, gradually lost his power and the organization atrophied.

In January 1943, Himmler visited Warsaw and ordered the total dissolution of the ghetto. The Jewish quarter was to be torn down immediately. No Poles were to be permitted to settle there, for Himmler did not want Warsaw to grow back to its former size.

It was assumed by the German High Command that the sixty thousand to seventy thousand Jews remaining in the ghetto would submit docilely to Himmler's orders. But they did not. In a resistance that must take its place among the heroic legends of the ages, these almost defenseless people stood and fought with unbelievable courage and tenacity.

Perhaps no one has left a more authoritative account of the Warsaw ghetto rebellion than the SS officer charged with smashing it. Juergen Stroop, SS Brigadefuehrer and Major General of Police, kept a day-to-day account of the

254

action. His official report, bound in leather, profusely illustrated and typed on seventy-five pages of heavy bond paper has survived. It is entitled "The Warsaw Ghetto Is No More."

When General Stroop first learned that the occupants of the ghetto refused to give themselves up, he expected that with the forces at his command he could break down all resistance in one day, and certainly three days would be more than ample. At his disposal he had 2,090 men, about half of them Regular Army or Waffen SS troops and the rest SS police reinforced by 335 Lithuanian militia and some Polish police and firemen.

For ordnance he had, in addition to the standard small arms and machine guns, several heavy armored cars, one 10-centimeter howitzer, one flame thrower, three 2.28-centimeter AA guns, at least one French tank, and engineering and demolition equipment.

The Germans had by now reduced the size of the walled-in ghetto to an area measuring only one thousand by three hundred yards. It was honeycombed, though, with sewers, vaults, and cellars which the desperate Jews had converted into fortified points. From the various plants in which they had been employed they had collected enough chemicals to construct a supply of Molotov cocktails. Smuggled rifles and machine guns and a few handguns were their total armament. At dawn on April 17 Stroop attacked.

When we invaded the ghetto for the first time, the Jews and the Polish bandits succeeded in repelling the participating units, including tanks and armored cars, by a well-prepared concentration of fire. When I ordered a second

255

attack, about 0600 hours, I distributed the units, separated from each other by indicated lines, and charged them with combing out the whole of the ghetto, each unit for a certain part. Although firing commenced again. we now succeeded in combing out the blocks according to plan. The enemy was forced to retire from the roofs and elevated bases to the basements, dugouts, and sewers. I ordered a barrier dam constructed below the ghetto and filled with water, but the Jews frustrated this plan to a great extent by blowing up the valves. Late the first day we encountered rather heavy resistance, but it was quickly broken by a special raiding party.

The attacking forces now brought their artillery into play, so that with roofs crashing and walls toppling about them the defenders were compelled to take to dugouts and sewers to continue their resistance. The SS men tried to make these refugees untenable by flooding the sewers, introducing smoke candles, and pouring creosote into the water. Each day the besiegers captured large numbers of the Jews and liquidated them on the spot or sent them to the extermination center at Treblinka.

On April 22, the fifth day of the battle, an impatient and furious Himmler ordered Stroop to "comb out the ghetto with the greatest severity and relentless tenacity."

I therefore decided to destroy the entire Jewish area by setting every block on fire. . . . Not infrequently, the Jews stayed in the burning buildings until, because of the heat and the fear of being burned alive they preferred to jump down from the upper stories after having thrown mattresses and other upholstered articles into the street from the burning buildings. With their bones broken. they still tried to crawl across the street into blocks of buildings which had not yet been set on fire or were only partly in flames.

Our setting the block on fire achieved the result in the course of the night that these Jews whom we had not been able to find despite all our search operations left their hide-outs under the roofs, in the cellars, and elsewhere and appeared at the outside of the buildings, trying to escape the flames. Masses of them—entire families—were already aflame and jumped from the windows or endeavored to let themselves down by means of sheets tied together or the like. Steps had been taken so that these Jews as well as the remaining ones were liquidated at once. . . .

Over and over again we observed that Jews and bandits, despite the danger of being burned alive, preferred to return into the flames rather than risk being caught by us. . . .

Others of this cowardly race fired their arms until the last moment and then jumped into the street, sometimes from as far up as the fourth floor.

Somehow the resistance went on. On April 26, Stroop reported:

During today's operation several blocks of buildings were burned down. This is the only and final method which forces this trash and subhumanity to the surface. As in the preceding days, uncounted Jews were buried in the blown-up dugouts and, as can be observed time and time again, burned with this bag of Jews today. We have, in my opinion, caught a very considerable part of the bandits and lowest elements of the ghetto. Intervening darkness prevented immediate liquidation. . . .

In a number of cases the inmates of the dugouts were hardly in a condition when the dugout had been blown up to crawl to the surface. The captured Jews report that many of the inmates of the dugouts became insane from the heat, smoke, and explosions. . . .

The whole operation is rendered more difficult by the cunning way in which the Jews and bandits act: for instance, we discovered that the hearses which were used to collect the corpses lying around, at the same time bring living Jews to the Jewish cemetery, and thus they are enabled to escape from the ghetto. Now this way of escape is also barred by continuous control of the hearses. . . .

All the Jews caught today were forcibly pulled out of dugouts. Not a single one gave himself up voluntarily, after his dugout had been opened. A considerable part of the Jews caught were pulled out of sewers. In one case the engineers laid a large explosive charge and proceeded to an adjoining entrance where they had something to do. In the meantime a Jew from the sewer removed the fuse and appropriated the charge. In the further course of this operation we succeeded in catching this Jew, still in possession of the explosive.

Then, summing up the day's operation: "1,330 Jews pulled out of dugouts and immediately destroyed, 362 Jews killed in battle. Caught today altogether: 1,722 Jews. This brings the total of Jews caught to 29,186. Moreover, it is very probable that numerous Jews have perished in the thirteen dugouts blown up today and in the conflagration. At the time of writing not one of the Jews caught still remains within Warsaw."

Stroop was continually amazed and angered by the unreasonable stubbornness of the Jews. He noted that some would

jump from the burning windows and balconies, abusing Germany and the Fuehrer and cursing the German soldiers.

258

If the Jews are requested to leave their dugout voluntarily, they hardly ever obey: they can only be forced to do so by the use of smoke candles.

Whereas it had been possible during the first days to catch considerable numbers of the Jews, who are cowards by nature, it became more and more difficult during the second half of the action to capture the bandits and Jews. A Jewess, upon being arrested in a dugout, quick as lightning put her hand under her skirt, as many others had done, and fetched from her bloomers a "pineapple" hand grenade, drew the safety catch, threw the grenade among the men who were searching her, and jumped quickly to cover.

Over and over again new battle groups consisting of twenty to thirty or more Jewish fellows, eighteen to twenty-five years of age, accompanied by a corresponding number of women, kindled new resistance. These battle groups were under orders to put up armed resistance to the last and if necessary to escape arrest by committing suicide. . . .

One such battle group succeeded in mounting a truck by ascending from a sewer in the so-called Presta, and in escaping with it (about 30–35 bandits). One bandit who had arrived with this truck exploded two hand grenades, which was the agreed signal, and the bandits and Jews—there were Polish bandits among these gangs armed with carbines, small arms and in one case, a light machine gun—mounted the truck and drove away in an unknown direction.

On May 3, German police dogs and sound detectors located the bunker of Berek Snaidmil's group at Franciszkanska 30. During the ensuing fighting Berek's abdomen was torn open by a hand grenade.

As the group prepared to withdraw, his comrades tried to carry him with them. Berek drew his revolver and

259

waved it at them. "Don't forget to take this," he shouted. "Keep fighting." Then he thrust the revolver into his mouth and pulled the trigger.

"Time and again the Jews try to escape even through burning buildings," Stroop reported on May 4. "Innumerable Jews whom we saw on the roofs during the conflagration perished in the flames. Others emerged from the upper stories at the last possible moment and were only able to escape death in the flames by jumping down. Today we caught a total of 2,283 Jews, of whom 204 were shot, and uncounted numbers of Jews were destroyed in dugouts and in the flames. The sum total of Jews caught rises to 44,089."

As late as May 8, Stroop wrote, "a number of subhumans, bandits, and terrorists still remain in the dugouts where the heat has become intolerable by reason of the fires." But he proclaimed that "the undersigned is determined to press on with the operation until the last Jew has been destroyed."

The general's report is accompanied by a series of photographs showing various phases of the battle. Scene after scene taken by German photographers depicts flaming buildings, broken-boned men and women lying on the streets unable to move, children holding up their hands in terror, victims lined up against a wall to be shot. Yet the few who remained alive still refused to bow their heads to their oppressors.

General Stroop reported on May 9, "The resistance offered by the Jews has not weakened today. 42 bunkers discovered. 1,037 Jews and bandits captured alive. 319

shot in the fighting. Total: 51,313. 254 Jews and bandits shot outside the ghetto."

On May 10 a group of ghetto fighters led by Abrasha Blum and Marek Edelman made their way through the sewers to Prosta Street. With the help of guides they negotiated the barbed-wire obstructions and booby traps, but the trucks which were to pick them up at night were delayed. They had to remain for eight hours in the sewer pipes, twenty-eight inches high.

The trucks finally arrived and took the fighters to the Lomyanki Forest near Warsaw, where they could harass the Germans from the rear. But Blum could not bear being separated from his wife and two children. He wormed his way back into the ghetto, and finally was trapped by the enemy. He made a rope of bedsheets to lower himself from a window but had to jump from the third story. He broke his legs and was machine-gunned by the Germans.

Finally, on May 16 at 2015 hours, the Germans blew up the Jewish synagogue and silence settled over Warsaw. The Aktion had ended. Not one of the valiant defenders was alive. Stroop was able to conclude his report:

"Only through the continuous and untiring work of all involved did we succeed in catching a total of 56,065 Jews whose extermination can be proved. To this should be added the number of Jews who lost their lives in explosions or fires but whose numbers could not be ascertained."

✡ On the Trail of Korczak ✡

✡

I first heard about Janusz Korczak and his orphans in the winter of 1965 while at dinner in Berlin with Artur Brauner, a film producer. Mr. Brauner was born in Poland and had barely escaped from Warsaw with his life in 1942. His film studio, CCC, is on the site of a former poison-gas factory. From his office window he is able every morning to look down on Spandau Prison where convicted former Nazis are serving life sentences. The proximity of his office to the prison is no coincidence; Mr. Brauner claims he likes to "keep an eye on the bastards."

Like most Jews in Germany today, Mr. Brauner rarely talks about the past. On this night at dinner, however, he reminisced about his hero, Janusz Korczak. I had never heard of Korczak and said so. Mr. Brauner told me enough of Korczak's story to excite my interest and curiosity.

Some days later I received from Mr. Brauner a copy of Korczak's diary kept in the ghetto from May to August 1942. The diary had been discovered fifteen years after the war hidden in a wall of the orphanage at Bielany.

Korczak wrote the diary in his small office which was also his bedroom and the orphanage infirmary. Frequently sick children whom he had to isolate from the rest shared his quarters. It is scarcely credible that Korczak still possessed the energy to write but what he wrote was a counterpoint to the horror of ghetto life. He was concerned solely with the safety and lives of his children. His diary notes were about intimate details of orphanage and ghetto life. In the flood of total bestiality he tried to find a ripple of intelligence and humanity.

The frequent references to his early years touched me personally because he was a third-generation assimilated Jew who, if asked if he was a Jew or a Pole, would answer, "I am a Pole." He was typical of the Jews of Germany, Poland, Russia, America, and England who considered themselves citizens of their countries rather than Jews.

Many of these people were only vaguely aware of their Jewishness until someone pointed a finger at them and said, "Jew, stand up and be counted." This happened to me once during the early years of World War II at an

Army camp in the United States. I have never forgotten the shock I had when I realized that the sergeant who was pointing the finger meant me. I had lost all identity as a person or as another GI. To him, I was a Jew, later to become "the Jew" in my outfit.

I kept thinking of Korczak until his story became an obsession and I started this book. Locating the scattered group who had known him was not as difficult as I anticipated. Their love for the old doctor is a strong bond, and one person sent me to another. Ultimately the trail led me to Israel, Germany, Spain, France, Poland, and England where I interviewed ghetto survivors who knew or had worked with Korczak. It is a measure of the man that of some sixty people I interviewed who had personal contact with him, everyone was either a teacher or in some way engaged in working with children.

To reconstruct Korczak's life for this book I have relied almost entirely upon the testimony of ghetto survivors and on his own fragmentary diary. I offer my sincere thanks to the following individuals and organizations to whom I am most indebted for their time and assistance.

WARSAW

Korczak's gentle heroism has inspired several plays and books in Poland, the most notable being Hanna Mortkowicz-Olczakow's *Mister Doctor*. In 1957 Korczak's biography, including a small selection of his works and sixty-two pages from his diary, was published in Warsaw by his old friend, Igor Newerly Abramov. There are mentions of Korczak and the children in most of the books written about the Warsaw ghetto. Emanuel Ringleblum's *Notes from the Warsaw Ghetto*, which is justifiably the most famous, was also the most helpful in describing that terrible time.

I was apprehensive over the reception I would find in Warsaw last summer when it became known I was writing a book about Korczak. To my pleasure and surprise I discovered that even though the government was officially anti-Zionist and historically anti-Semitic, Korczak is, nevertheless, considered a hero. The orphanages which he founded are still in existence, operated on much the same lines he established. New orphanages bearing his name and dedicated to his memory are planned. And his books for children are still popular in Poland.

The Korczak Committee in Warsaw proved to be a treasure house of information and memorabilia. The steel-rimmed glasses with the cracked left lens which Korczak forgot on the day of the evacuation are part of the collection, along with many handwritten medical reports compiled over a period of years which he had planned to turn into a book. The committee also has copies of most of the twenty-four books written by Korczak and much original manuscript material.

Ela Frydman, one of the founders of the Korczak Committee, is a tiny, bright-eyed, intense lady with a warm sense of humor who has devoted much of her time to keeping the name of Korczak alive. She has scrapbooks of clippings from all over the world indicating the success of her mission.

Sofia Dorosz, a friend of Miss Frydman's, dropped in at the committee's modest offices one day for lunch and donated that afternoon and several others helping me on

266

interviews, translating Polish into a wonderfully pure English which she learned in England as a schoolgirl but had not used for many years.

Colonel Michael Wroblewski had never told his story before, preferring instead to keep his souvenirs of Korczak as personal memories for fear they might be misinterpreted. But at the prompting of Mmes. Frydman and Dorosz, he helped fill in gaps in the doctor's last day of life in the ghetto.

Mr. Aleksander Ford is one of the leading film directors of Poland with a reputation throughout the world. One of his big dreams has been to direct a movie about the life of Korczak. At this writing, such a movie is now in progress, directed by Mr. Ford with Artur Brauner as producer. Mrs. Ford is an American who yearns for copies of the current American journals but loves her life in Poland. She was most valuable helping translate several difficult passages in Korczak's works into English for me.

Damita Dabrowska and the Jewish Historical Institute where I found copies of old ghetto newspapers which enabled me to document much of Zygmunt Friedrych's journey to Treblinka.

Mrs. Maria Falkasawa, director of the Orphan's Home at Krochmalna 92, founded by Korczak in 1911, was also helpful. The orphanage was being redecorated and was in a state of chaos, but Mrs. Falkasawa created sufficient order and mood for me to believe that for the time I was with her Korczak still lived.

Sierdzki Zdistaw, director of Our Home in Bielany, struggled patiently with our language difficulties but by his own example demonstrated the Korczak system of education. I had ridden on the streetcar to Bielany without putting in a token. He took me back to my hotel by streetcar and slipped in an additional token to cover my free ride.

The Museum of the History of the Polish Movement is on the site of the old Gestapo Headquarters. Many of the rooms where Nazi interrogations took place have been kept intact with their horrible tools for torture. Even the scribbles on the cell walls remain.

Although I never met Christine Cenkalska, her translations of Polish documents relating to Korczak were most helpful.

On the last day of my visit to Poland the strangest witness of all sought me out at the Grand Hotel. He called from the lobby and in broken English asked if I was the American writing about Janusz Korczak. Assured that I was and that I would shield his identity, he agreed to meet me in the hotel lobby; I was to carry a book in my left hand and he would contact me. Apparently I passed his test, and he led me to the dining room which at that time of day was closed to business. Isolated at a table in the center of the room, his story came bursting out in a combination of English and German. He was the Jewish policeman who had accompanied the orphans on their last march. He lives today in Warsaw, as an Aryan.

LONDON

The Wiener Library was founded in 1933 by Dr. Alfred Wiener, a refugee from Nazi persecution. The library's documentary collections on every aspect of Nazi policy and history are world famous and during World War II

268

the collection was virtually a part of the British Ministry of Information. The library was most useful to me in providing a varied collection of signed documents from ghetto survivors plus unpublished photographs.

The Polish Library occupies a large, solid, stucco mansion on the right side of Hyde Park in London. The house is full of books and old copies of Polish newspapers from the war period which were helpful in providing information and a basis for checking facts.

P. G. de Lotz spent hours on his own time searching for out-of-print books which he then sent on to me as part of a service he provides for authors.

Michael Zylberberg, author of a play about Korczak entitled "Melody of a Doomed City," was forced to flee Warsaw in April 1943. Mr. Zylberberg was a friend and neighbor of Korczak's as well as a prime mover in ghetto circles. I am particularly thankful for his description of the events which he witnessed following the suicide of Adam Czerniakow. He also provided me with valuable insights into his old friend although there was a conflict of interests as Mr. Zylberberg is now preparing a book about his own life in the ghetto.

SPAIN

Elizabeth Bagney had once attended one of Korczak's summer camps and gave me a graphic demonstration of camp life and the Code of Justice. Now a social worker, Mrs. Bagney delayed her departure for the summer camp she runs in Murguia, Spain, in order to toil through scrapbooks to find mementos of interest which she then translated into English.

GERMANY

A. R. B. Smith of Berlin translated into English General Stroop's diary report, "The Warsaw Ghetto Is No More," and also labored mightily to translate Korczak's diary, spending hours checking on the proper meaning of certain words to assure the accuracy of his contribution.

The Institut für Zeitgeschichte, Munich, has an almost unparalleled collection of Nazi documents. Dr. H. Hoch was unfailing with his time and patience and aided greatly in finding documents and pictures which gave me background for my portrayal of SS Untersturmfuehrer Erwin Schneider.

UNITED STATES

Arnost Horlik was a lawyer for the War Crimes Commission and tried seven Nazi criminals at Nuremberg. Dapper, precise, and fair to a fault, Mr. Horlik gave me the benefit of his scholarship and level-headed thinking as well as companionship and guidance.

Shimeon Brisman, a Polish refugee himself, is now a mainstay of the UCLA Research Library's Department on Jewish Studies, where I found the only English editions of Korczak's fairy tales.

Dr. Abraham I. Katsh is president of the Dropsie College in Philadelphia. His lectures at NYU two decades ago in Jewish History and Hebrew Culture bore fruit in this book.

Betty and Sergei Nutkiewicz escaped from the ghetto in 1942 and are now prominent social workers in Los Angeles. Mrs. Nutkiewicz helped locate and translate documents and Mr. Nutkiewicz carefully and patiently gave me an insight into the life of the ghetto.

And my special gratitude to Brooks Roberts of Ardsley, New York, who encouraged me when I needed it most and who, as always, gave untiringly of his valuable talents as a friend and editor.

ISRAEL

The Israeli Publisher's catalogue lists some fourteen works of Korczak translated into Hebrew. Shmuel Raz gave up many of his evenings while a student at UCLA to translate these books aloud into a tape recorder. When the Six Day War commenced, Shmuel, who was a frogman in Israel's small navy, gave up his studies at UCLA to return to his own country. After the war he was of invaluable assistance to me in helping to locate and interview Israelis who knew Korczak.

Gershon Langsfelder, the pipe-smoking, mild-mannered chief of Israel Police, Department for Investigation of Nazi War Crimes, Beyt Dagon, read through the statements of hundreds of Poles seeking mentions of Korczak.

Dr. Y. Krmish of Yad Vashem Institute of Archives, Jerusalem, donated hours of his time and allowed me to read the unpublished diary of Adam Czerniakow.

Fega Lipschitz who lives at Kibbutz Eyn Harod roused herself from a sick bed and devoted hours to telling me of orphanage life and Korczak's visits to Israel, and she was most helpful in giving me an understanding of Stefa Wilczynska, Korczak's right hand.

Joseph Heilpern Arnon who is a psychologist and worked for three years with Korczak at Krochmalna 92

271

gave me much valuable insight into the doctor's character and the forces which shaped his life and personality.

Jonas Turkow, a prominent actor and author, allowed me to read his notes for a soon-to-be published story about his friend and neighbor.

Zvi Wasser, who was secretary of Emanuel Ringleblum and the ghetto underground in the 1939–43 period, added much to my knowledge of Korczak's last day.

Wladyslaw Friedheim, secretary general of CENTOS, gave me insight into Korczak's relations with the ghetto community.

Helena Szereszewska allowed me to read her personal diary of the period and permitted an excerpt to be used.

Israel Shmuel Zyngman entertained as well as enlightened with his stories about life in the orphanage.

Irene Halperin for her poignant recollection of Korczak's last days.

Yaacov Ben Joseph, principal of a high school in Tel Aviv and a former student at Korczak's, remembered his lessons well and retained some of his original notes from lectures.

Dr. Adolf Abraham Berman made available to me a transcript of his report to the War Crimes Commission on the dissolution of the ghetto.

I spent an afternoon last summer in the Tel Aviv apartment of Samy Gogol. It was an unusual gathering. All of the guests had lived in Warsaw, and most of them had at least one number tattooed on their forearms or shoulders. Some, like Samy, had survived seven concentration camps before coming to Israel, the one place in the world they felt welcome.

It was a particularly happy day for Samy and his wife. Their son, a commando lieutenant, had returned wounded but alive from the Sinai Front. The terrible past seemed erased from the minds of these people sipping chocolate and eating cakes, watching their children play, and telling the personal jokes on each other that people who know and respect each other tell so well.

But alone in an interview with me they were different. There were many times while I uncovered the facts needed for this book that I hated myself for asking these good people to return into the torture chamber of memory. Many times a man or woman would pause to look at me with pain-filled eyes and say, "It is impossible to describe . . . you can't understand it if you weren't there . . ."

I would like to ask their forgiveness.